It's another Quality Book from CGP

This book is for anyone doing Key Stage Three German.

It contains lots of tricky questions designed
to make you sweat — because that's the only
way you'll get any better.

It's also got a couple of daft bits in to try and make the whole
experience at least vaguely entertaining for you.

What CGP is all about

Our sole aim here at CGP is to produce the highest quality
books — carefully written, immaculately presented and
dangerously close to being funny.

Then we work our socks off to get them out to you
— at the cheapest possible prices.

Contents

SECTION 6 — PHONE CALLS AND LETTERS

SECTION 7 — WEATHER, HOLIDAYS AND COUNTRIES

SECTION 8 — GRAMMAR AND PHRASES

Published by CGP

Editor:

James Paul Wallis

Contributors:

Taissa Csáky
Bettina Hermoso Gomez
Louise Mycock
Sheila Brighten

With thanks to Iryna Csáky and Rachel Thompson for the proofreading.

ISBN: 978 1 84146 849 5

Groovy website: www.cgpbooks.co.uk
Jolly bits of clipart from CorelDRAW®
Printed by Elanders Ltd, Newcastle upon Tyne.

Based on the classic CGP style created by Richard Parsons.

Numbers

Q1 Match the German words to numbers from the box. I've done the first one for you.

a) dreiundsiebzig ......73......   f) sechsundachtzig ....

b) zweiundneunzig ....   g) drei ....

c) zwölf ....   h) zehn ....

d) einunddreißig ....   i) fünf ....

e) fünfundzwanzig ....   j) sechzehn ....

> 31   92   25   86   3   10   12   16   5   73

Q2 Write out these numbers as words in German. I've done the first one for you.

a) 7 _sieben_   e) 37 ....   i) 41 ....

b) 23 ....   f) 91 ....   j) 72 ....

c) 89 ....   g) 58 ....   k) 1 ....

d) 14 ....   h) 17 ....   l) 100 ....

Q3 Match the German words to numbers from the box. I've done the first one for you.

a) zehnte ......10th......   e) neunte ....

b) achte ....   f) dritte ....

c) siebte ....   g) vierzehnte ....

d) fünfte ....   h) zwölfte ....

> 9th   3rd   12th   10th   14th   1st   7th   8th   5th

Q4 Write out these numbers as words in German. Guess what — I've gone and done the first one for you.

a) 18th _achtzehnte_   d) 6th ....

b) 11th ....   e) 4th ....

c) 2nd ....   f) 1st ....

"It's a 12" — "We don't believe you"... (The boy who cried zwölf)

Numbers like forty-six are said <u>backwards</u> in German — <u>sechsundvierzig</u> (literally "six-and-forty").
It looks weird, but you get used to it. Think of the song, "four-and-twenty blackbirds". Tasty...

2

Time and Dates

For each clock, say what time it is, in German.
[Don't just write the time, say "It is ...".] I've done the first one for you.

Watch Out: in German you say "half to" not "half past", e.g. "halb zwei" = "half past one".

a) *Es ist elf Uhr* ....

e) ....

b) ....

f) ....

c) ....

g) ....

d) ....

h) ....

Q2 Write out the time shown on each clock in full, using the 24-hour clock, in German. I've done the first one for you.

a) **01:45** *ein Uhr fünfundvierzig* .....
....

c) **11:55** ....
....

b) **22:25** ....
....

d) **13:00** ....
....

Q3 Translate these German expressions of time into English.

a) morgen
....

e) Nachmittag
....

i) Morgen
....

b) Woche
....

f) Tag
....

j) Nacht
....

c) Abend
....

g) heute
....

k) gestern
....

d) Monat
....

h) Wochenende
....

l) Jahr
....

Section 1 — Basic Stuff

Times and Dates

Q1 Write these German months out in English.

a) Mai .... e) Juli .... i) Juni ....

b) Januar .... f) Februar .... j) September ....

c) Oktober .... g) März .... k) November ....

d) April .... h) August .... l) Dezember ....

Q2 Days of the week — match the German words to the English ones on the right. I've done the first one for you.

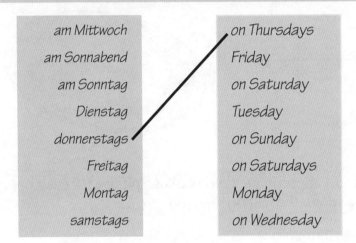

am Mittwoch   on Thursdays

am Sonnabend   Friday

am Sonntag   on Saturday

Dienstag   Tuesday

donnerstags   on Sunday

Freitag   on Saturdays

Montag   Monday

samstags   on Wednesday

Q3 Write out these dates as words in German. I've done the first one for you.

a) on the thirty-first of December   *am einunddreißigsten Dezember* ....

b) on the sixteenth of April   ....

c) on the first of July   ....

d) on the twenty-eighth of February   ....

e) on the third of September   ....

f) on the twenty-ninth of May   ....

Don't Forget
For a date that's 20th or above, it ends "sten", e.g. 24th = vierundzwanzigsten

Q4 Answer these questions with a date in German. Write all the words out in full.

a) What date is Christmas Day? ....

b) What date is New Year's Day? ....

c) What date is Bonfire Night? ....

4

Meeting and Greeting

Q1   Here are two lists of ways to say hello. Draw lines to match the English on the left to the German words on the right. I've done the first one for you.

Hello / Good day	Guten Abend
Good morning	Guten Tag
Hi	Hallo
Good evening	Guten Morgen

Q2   Write these "goodbye" words out in German. Choose from the words in the ellipse. I've done the first one for you.

a) bye   *tschüss* ....

b) goodbye   ....

c) see you later ....

d) good night   ....

auf gute später Wiedersehen bis Nacht tschüss

Q3   Read these situations and write the most appropriate hello/goodbye phrase for each one. Don't use the same phrase twice. I've done the first one for you.

a) You've been to the cinema with some German mates and now you're all going home.   *bis später*

b) You greet your German penpal's parents when you arrive home for dinner after 5 p.m.   ....

c) Time for bed. What are you going to say to your penpal's family?   ....

d) It's 9 a.m. the next morning and you want to buy a drink at the shop. How do you greet the shopkeeper?   ....

e) You meet your German mates at the local shopping centre the next day. What do you say to them when you first see them?   ....

f) You see your penpal's teacher out shopping at 1 p.m. Be polite and greet him.   ....

g) You're at the airport about to leave Germany now. Time to say goodbye to your penpal's parents.   ....

h) Now you're saying goodbye to your German penpal at the airport. What do you say? (Try not to get too emotional!)   ....

Meeting and Greeting

Q1 Use the words in the blob to finish off these sentences.

danke schön dir geht geht's

a) Gut, ...

b) Wie geht es .... ?

c) Wie .... ?

d) Wie .... es Ihnen?

e) .... , Sie kennen zu lernen.

Q2 Read these situations and match them to the most appropriate German sentence(s) in the box. Use each sentence once.

a) You're introducing Bernd to your German teacher. ....

b) You're introducing a female friend to your penpal's parents. ....

c) You're introducing Bernd to your younger brother and his friends. ....

d) You're introducing Bernd to your best friend who's the same age as you. ....

Darf ich dir Bernd vorstellen?   *Darf ich Ihnen Bernd vorstellen?*

Darf ich euch Bernd vorstellen?   *Darf ich Ihnen meine Freundin vorstellen?*

Q3 Read these situations and write the most appropriate German sentence for each one. Don't use the same expression twice. I've done the first one for you.

a) *I feel like we've known each other ages now we're up to page 5. I want to introduce my good friend Ursula to you. What do I say? (Assume we're the same age.)*

   Darf ich dir Ursula vorstellen?

b) *You're glad to meet Ursula. What do you say to her to show this? (You don't need to be formal.)*

   ....

c) *You've just been introduced to the mayor of a German town. How do you say, "Pleased to meet you"?*

   ....

d) *You ask the mayor how he's doing. He doesn't seem very matey, so make sure you keep it formal.*

   ....

e) *Being polite, the mayor's asked you how you're doing too. You're well, so how do you say that in German?*

   ....

Being Polite

Q1   Here are two lists of polite expressions. Draw lines to match the English on the left to the German on the right. I've done the first one for you.

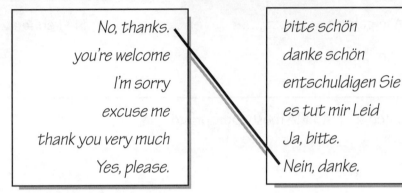

No, thanks.	bitte schön
you're welcome	danke schön
I'm sorry	entschuldigen Sie
excuse me	es tut mir Leid
thank you very much	Ja, bitte.
Yes, please.	Nein, danke.

Q2   Write in the missing words in these polite expressions.
(No looking at Q1. Cheating's for wimps.)

a) es tut mir ....

b) danke............................

c) Nein, ...

d) bitte ....

e) .... , bitte.

f) .... Sie

Q3   Some people have no manners. Make these conversations polite instead of rude
— rewrite the underlined bits, or fill in the blanks. I've done the first one for you.

a) Hans: Möchtest du eine Orange?
Julia: <u>Nein.</u>
   Nein, danke
   ....

b) Andreas: <u>Wo ist das Museum?</u>
   ....

c) Karin: Danke.
Hans: ....
   ....

d) Monika: <u>Ich mag Äpfel nicht.</u>
   ....

e) Werner: Danke schön.
Hans: ....
   ....

f) Sabine: <u>Wo ist das Kino?</u>
   ....

g) Gerhard: Möchtest du eine Orange?
Thomas: <u>Ja.</u>
   ....

h) Erika: <u>Ich mag Karotten nicht.</u>
   ....

Hints:
eine Orange = an orange, das Museum = the museum,
Äpfel = apples, das Kino = the cinema, Karotten = carrots

Being Polite

Q1 Write these German phrases out in English. Choose from the phrases in the circle.

a) Ich will   ....

b) bitte   ....

c) Ich möchte   ....

d) Darf ich   ....

I would like
I want   *May I*
please

Q2 Read each of these situations and write down the most appropriate German sentence from the box. Use each sentence once.

a) You're sucking up to your host, so you ask if you can help lay the table.

....

b) Dinner turns out to be a joint of beef. Apologise and explain that you don't eat meat.

....

c) After a good night's sleep, you're ready for breakfast. Offer to help prepare the meal.

....

d) Ask if you can help with the washing up.

....

Darf ich Ihnen spülen helfen?   **Darf ich Ihnen helfen den Tisch zu decken?**   **Darf ich Ihnen helfen das Essen zubereiten?**   **Es tut mir Leid, aber ich esse Fleisch nicht.**

Q3 Politeness costs nothing and it'll stop you winding up your hosts. Rewrite these sentences to make them polite. I've done the first one for you.

a) You would like an apple.
DON'T SAY: "Ich will einen Apfel." BE POLITE: *Ich möchte einen Apfel.*

b) You would like to sit here.
DON'T SAY: "Ich will hier sitzen." BE POLITE: ....

c) You would like a roll.
DON'T SAY: "Ich will ein Brötchen." BE POLITE: ....

d) You would like to do the washing up.
DON'T SAY: "Ich will spülen." BE POLITE: ....

Your Details

Q1 Draw lines to match the German sentences on the left with their English meanings on the right.

Ich habe am dritten Mai Geburtstag.	I like football.
Was magst du?	I'm called Aleesha.
Ich heiße Aleesha.	What are you called?
Ich bin neunzehn Jahre alt.	My birthday is on the 3rd of May.
Wie heißt du?	When is your birthday?
Ich mag Fußball.	I am nineteen.
Wie alt bist du?	How old are you?
Wann hast du Geburtstag?	What do you like?

Q2 Use the words from the box to fill the gaps in these sentences. Use each word once.

a) Ich bin ....

b) Ich trage eine ....

c) Ich habe .... Augen.

d) Ich .... groß.

e) Ich habe .... Haare.

f) Ich bin nett und ....

> schwarze   klein   blaue   bin   Brille   fleißig

Q3 George has had a letter from his new German penpal Peter.
Read the letter, then put T (true) or F (false) for each of the sentences on the right.

Lieber George,

Ich heiße Peter. Ich bin fünfzehn Jahre alt. Ich habe am ersten Oktober Geburtstag. Ich mag Fußball und Tennis. Ich bin klein und dünn. Ich habe braune Augen und ich trage eine Brille. Ich habe blonde Haare.

Peter

a) Peter says he is fourteen. ☐

b) His birthday is on the 3rd of October. ☐

c) He likes tennis. ☐

d) He has brown eyes. ☐

e) He doesn't wear glasses. ☐

f) He has blond hair. ☐

Ich bin groß, ich bin fleißig — ich bin lying...

There are two bits 1) You say "I have on the 3rd of May birthday" (not "my birthday is...")
I find <u>tricky</u> here: 2) In English "glasses" is <u>plural</u>, but in German "eine Brille" is <u>singular</u>.

Your Family

Q1 Write down what these mean in English:

a) meine Schwester ....

b) meine Großmutter ....

c) meine Cousine ....

d) mein Freund ....

e) mein Onkel ....

f) meine Stiefmutter ....

g) mein Stiefbruder ....

Be this smart,
learn some German.

Q2 Read Petra's letter and then answer the questions in English:

a) How old is Petra? ....

b) Who is Peter? ....

c) Who is Louise? ....

d) What is her uncle's name? ....

e) Who is Rob? ....

f) Who is nice? ....

Liebe Sophie,

ich heiße Petra und ich bin zehn Jahre alt. Meine Mutter heißt Ann und mein Vater heißt Peter. Ich bin ein Einzelkind. Ich habe einen Onkel und eine Tante. Mein Onkel heißt Bob und meine Tante heißt Louise. Ich habe einen Cousin. Mein Cousin heißt Rob. Er ist nett.

Petra

Q3 Shivana has drawn a family tree. Fill in the missing bits. Each missing bit should say "my mother", "my cousin" etc. in German. I've done three of them for you.

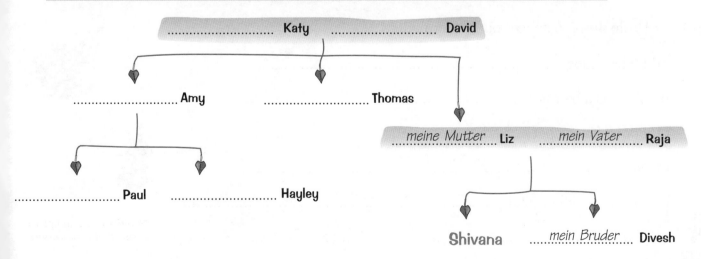

Pets and Animals

Q1 Write these pet words out again, filling in the missing letters.

a) das P_erd_ ....

c) der _und_ ....

b) die _au_ ....

d) die Kat_e ....

Q2 Write down the German word for each of these beasts, including the **der**, **die** or **das**.

a) ....

b) ....

c) ....

d) ....

e) ....

f) ....

Q3 Sort these words out to make sentences about pets. I've done the first one for you.

a) keine Haustiere habe ich

Ich habe keine Haustiere.

b) Kaninchen habe ein ich

....

c) einen hat sie Hamster

....

d) hast du eine Katze

....

e) ist Hund mein böse

....

f) Schildkröte "Speedy" meine heißt

....

Q4 Write these sentences out in German.

a) I have a dog. ....

b) She has a hamster. ....

c) I don't have a pet. ....

d) My bird is big. ....

e) My cat is called "Fluffy". ....

f) You have a dog. ....

"A demon's for life not just for Halloween"

Section 2 — You, Family and Home

Your Home

Q1 Draw lines to match the English words on the left to the German ones on the right. I've done the first one for you.

kitchen	das Schlafzimmer
dining room	die Küche
living room	das Wohnzimmer
bedroom	das Badezimmer
garden	der Garten
bathroom	das Esszimmer

Q2 Use the words from the box to fill in the blanks. Use each word once.

a) Zu Hause, gibt es .... Schlafzimmer.

b) Was für ein .... hast du?

c) .... Hause, gibt es eine ....

d) .... für ein Haus hast du?

e) Zu Hause, ... es ein Wohnzimmer.

f) Zu Hause, gibt .... zwei Wohnzimmer.

was
gibt
Zu
ein
es
Haus
Küche

Q3 Read the conversation between Renate and her friend Vincent, then answer the questions.

RENATE: Was für ein Haus hast du?
VINCENT: Zu Hause gibt es eine Küche, ein Wohnzimmer,
          ein Badezimmer und drei Schlafzimmer.
RENATE: Was für Möbel gibt es in deinem Schlafzimmer?
VINCENT: Es gibt ein Bett, einen Tisch, einen Kleiderschrank und einen Stuhl.

a) Does Vincent's house have a living room?   ....

b) How many bedrooms are there in Vincent's house?   ....

c) Does Vincent have two chairs in his bedroom?   ....

d) How many rooms are there altogether in Vincent's home? ....

e) How many items of furniture does Vincent have in his room? ....

Q4 Write at least three sentences to describe **your** house / flat, **in German**.

....

....

....

Section 2 — You, Family and Home

Where You Live

Q1   Write these sentences out **in English**.

 a) Ich wohne in einer Großstadt.   ....

 b) Ich wohne in einem Haus.   ....

 c) Ich lebe auf dem Land.   ....

 d) Ich wohne am Meer.   ....

 e) Ich wohne in einem Dorf.   ....

Q2   Now write these sentences out **in German**.

 a) I live in the mountains.   ....

 b) I live in London.   ....

 c) I live in Leeds, a city in the north of England.

     ....

 d) I like living here because it's fantastic.

     ....

 e) I don't like living here because it's too quiet.

     ....

Q3   Read these letters, then put **T** (true) or **F** (false) next to each of the sentences on the right.

Ich heiße Mark. Ich bin zehn Jahre alt. Ich wohne in einer Wohnung. Ich wohne in München, einer Großstadt in Deutschland. Ich lebe gern hier, weil es interessant ist.

 a) Mark lives in a city. ☐

 b) Mark lives in a house. ☐

 c) Mark doesn't like the place where he lives. ☐

 d) He thinks that the place where he lives is fantastic. ☐

Ich heiße Natalie. Ich bin vierzehn Jahre alt. Ich wohne in einem Haus. Ich wohne in einem Dorf in Nordwestengland. Ich lebe nicht gern hier, weil es langweilig ist.

 e) Natalie lives in a flat. ☐

 f) She lives in the south of England. ☐

 g) She doesn't like the place where she lives. ☐

 h) She thinks where she lives is boring. ☐

Daily Routine

Q1 Write these sentences out in the correct order. Start with what you do first thing in the morning, and finish with what you do last thing at night.

Ich esse Frühstück.　　　　1) ....

Ich gehe nach Hause.　　　2) ....

Ich sehe fern.　　　　　　3) ....

Ich ziehe mich an.　　　　4) ....

Ich wache auf.　　　　　　5) ....

Ich gehe ins Bett.　　　　6) ....

Ich stehe auf.　　　　　　7) ....

Ich gehe in die Schule.　　8) ....

"Maybe later I'll ask Connie to p.35 with me..."

Q2 Write these out in German:

a) I wash myself. ....

b) I eat dinner. ....

c) I do my homework. ....

d) I get dressed. ....

e) I go to bed. ....

f) I walk to school. ....

g) I wake up. ....

h) I eat breakfast. ....

Q3 Bob's German penfriend has written him a letter about his everyday activities. Read the letter and answer the questions.

Ich wache um sieben Uhr auf.
Ich stehe um sieben Uhr dreißig auf.
Ich wasche mich um Viertel vor acht.
Ich ziehe mich um acht Uhr an.
Ich esse Frühstück um acht Uhr dreißig. Ich gehe um Viertel vor neun in die Schule. Ich gehe nach Hause um fünf Uhr. Um sechs Uhr sehe ich fern und esse mein Abendessen.
Ich gehe um neun Uhr ins Bett.

a) When does he wake up?　　　..............

b) What does he do at a quarter to nine?　..............

c) What does he do at half past eight?　..............

d) When does he eat dinner?　　..............

e) What does he do at five?　　..............

f) What does he do at a quarter to eight?　..............

g) When does he go to bed?　　..............

Chores

Q1 Match up the German phrases in the middle with the English meanings to each side. I've done the first one for you.

I wash the car

I do the cleaning

I make my bed

I wash the dishes

Ich putze.
Ich mache nichts.
Ich spüle.
Ich mache mein Bett.
Ich sauge Staub.
Ich räume mein Zimmer auf.
Ich gehe einkaufen.
Ich wasche das Auto.

I don't do anything

I do the shopping

I tidy my room

I do the vacuum cleaning

Q2 Put the following words in the correct order so that you can make a sentence about "chores". I've done the first one for you.

a) wasche Auto Ich das

Ich wasche das Auto.

b) decke den Ich Tisch

....

c) mache Ich Bett mein

....

d) putze Ich

....

e) spüle Ich

....

f) Zimmer räume auf mein Ich

....

Q3 Complete the following sentences, using the words from the box:

a) Ich .... das Auto.

b) Ich mache ....

c) Ich .... mein Bett.

d) Ich ....

e) Ich .... Staub.

f) Ich .... den Tisch.

sauge   decke
nichts   wasche
mache   putze

Q4 Write out these sentences in German.

a) I wash the dishes.

....

b) I do the cleaning

....

c) I don't do anything.

....

d) I lay the table.

....

Section 2 — You, Family and Home

The Body

Q1 Look at the picture of the body, and choose words from the box to fill in each of the missing labels.

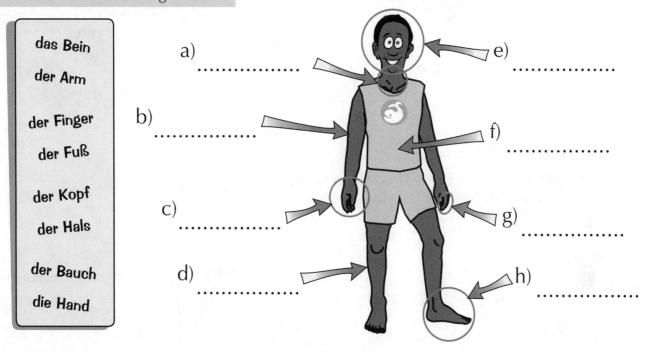

das Bein

der Arm

der Finger

der Fuß

der Kopf

der Hals

der Bauch

die Hand

a) ....

b) ....

c) ....

d) ....

e) ....

f) ....

g) ....

h) ....

Q2 Write these out in German. Don't forget the **der**, **die** or **das**.

a) the knee ....

b) the leg ....

c) the back ....

d) the finger ....

e) the stomach ....

f) the throat ....

Q3 Label Peter's head in German. Remember to write "der", "das" or "die" in front of the word.

a) ....

b) ....

c) ....

d) ....

e) ....

f) ....

So that's why it's called Fußball — not 'cos they moan...

Ah, come on, this is almost <u>fun</u>. Writing out "<u>der Finger</u>" is <u>1000</u> times better than trying to spell "das Vereinigte Königreich" for the third time in a row. Go on, allow yourself a little grin for once.

Health and Illness

Q1 Draw lines to match the English on the left to the German on the right. I've done the first one for you.

chemist's   das Krankenhaus

hospital   Ich will zum Arzt gehen

I want to go to the doctor's   Ich bin krank

doctor ———— der Arzt

I am ill   die Apotheke

Learn some German, it might help you feel better.

Q2 On each picture, the cross show where the person hurts. Write out the sentence from the box that says how they're feeling.

a) ....

b) ....

c) ....

d) ....

e) ....

Ich habe Bauchschmerzen.

Mein Hals tut mir weh.

Ich habe Kopfschmerzen.

Mein Rücken tut mir weh.

Mein Finger tut mir weh.

Q3 Write these out in English:

a) das Rezept ....

b) das Pflaster ....

c) die Tablette ....

d) die Salbe ....

e) das Medikament ....

f) die Schmerztablette ....

Q4 Write these phrases out in German.

a) I have stomachache

....

b) My nose hurts

....

c) I have earache

....

d) My leg hurts

....

e) My back hurts

....

f) I have a headache

....

School Subjects

Q1 Draw lines to match up the German on the left to the English on the right. I've done the first one for you.

Dear Mum, today at school I got a new hairstyle...

(die) Physik
(die) Geografie
(das) Englisch
(die) Kunst
(das) Deutsch
(die) Geschichte
(die) Mathe

English
maths
history
art
German
physics
geography

Q2 Here are some school subjects in English. Write down what they are in German.

a) *ICT*

....

b) *chemistry*

....

c) *science*

....

d) *music*

....

e) *biology*

....

f) *religious studies*

....

g) *sport*

....

h) *French*

....

i) *Spanish*

....

Q3 Read the letter, then answer the questions on the right.

Ich heiße Renate und ich bin vierzehn Jahre alt.

In der Schule habe ich viele Schulfächer. Ich treibe Sport, Englisch, Naturwissenschaft, Musik, Deutsch und Informatik.

Ich mag Sport, weil er einfach ist. Ich hasse Englisch, weil es langweilig ist. Mein Lieblingsfach ist Musik, weil sie interessant ist.

a) Which language does Renate study in school? ....

b) Does she do maths? ....

c) Does she like sports? ....

d) Which is her favourite subject? ....

e) Which subject doesn't she like? ....

f) Why doesn't she like it? ....

g) Why does she like music? ....

School Routine

Q1   For each German phrase, write the letter of the English phrase which matches it.

     i)   Ich stehe um sieben Uhr auf. ☐

     ii)   Ich fahre mit dem Bus zur Schule. ☐

     iii)   Die Schule fängt um acht Uhr an. ☐

     iv)   Wir machen eine Stunde Hausaufgaben pro Tag. ☐

     v)   Jede Stunde dauert fünfzig Minuten. ☐

     vi)   Die Schule ist um drei Uhr aus. ☐

     vii)   Ich gehe zu Fuß zur Schule. ☐

A *School begins at 8.00*

B *I get up at seven o'clock.*

C *I go to school by bus.*

D *I go to school on foot.*

E *School ends at three o'clock.*

F *We do one hour of homework every day.*

G *Each lesson lasts fifty minutes.*

Q2   Fill in the gaps in these sentences. Choose from the words in the blob.

     a)   Ich fahre mit dem .... zur Schule.

     b)   Wir haben neun .... pro Tag.

     c)   Die Schule .... um acht Uhr an.

     d)   Ich gehe zu .... zur Schule.

     e)   Jede Stunde dauert vierzig ....

     f)   Ich .... um acht Uhr auf.

Stunden Minuten fängt Fahrrad Fuß stehe

Q3   Imagine tomorrow is your first day in school. You've made some notes in your diary to remember what you have to do tomorrow. Write them out in German.

     7.00   Get up ....

     7.30   Have breakfast ....

     8.30   School begins ....

     3.00   School finishes ....

     We have 7 lessons per day. ....

Q4   Now your turn — say what your school day is like (what time school begins, when it finishes, etc.). ...But do it in German.

....

....

....

Classroom Stuff

Q1 If your teacher yelled the following things at you, what would you do or say? Underline the correct meaning in English.

a)   ***steht auf!*** = Stand up! // Sit down!

b)   ***seid ruhig!*** = Be quiet! // Listen!

c)   ***Wie sagt man das auf Deutsch?***
= What does that mean? // How do you say that in German?

d)   ***Was bedeutet das?***
= What does that mean? // How do you say that in English?

e)   ***hört zu!*** = Be quiet! // Listen!

f)   ***setzt euch!*** = Stand up! // Sit down!

Be this small,
learn some German.

Q2 All these words are some kind of "classroom stuff". Write down what they are in English.

a) der Stundenplan   d) das Lineal   g) der Lehrer

....

b) der Kuli   e) ein Übungsheft

....

c) der Gummi   f) das Buch

....

Q3 Write these out in German:

a) How do you say that in German?   f) teacher (woman)   ....

....   g) pupil (bloke)   ....

b) Stand up! ....   h) pencil   ....

c) right   ....   i) uniform   ....

d) What does that mean?   j) timetable   ....

....   k) In the classroom   ....

e) Listen! ....

Jobs

Q1 These are the names of jobs for **MEN**. Write out what they mean in English.

a) Mechaniker .... f) Bauarbeiter ....

b) Verkäufer .... g) Zahnarzt ....

c) Schauspieler .... h) Polizist ....

d) Friseur .... i) Sekretär ....

e) Ingenieur .... j) Arzt ....

Q2 These are the names of jobs for **WOMEN**. Write out what they mean in English.

a) Friseuse .... f) Krankenschwester ....

b) Schauspielerin .... g) Ärztin ....

c) Büroangestellte .... h) Polizistin ....

d) Bauarbeiterin .... i) Ingenieurin ....

e) Verkäuferin .... j) Lehrerin ....

Q3 Here you have a list of jobs in German. Write them out in the correct column, depending whether they're words for MEN or for WOMEN. I've done the first one for you.

Büroangestellter   Krankenpfleger

Bauarbeiterin   Arzt

Krankenschwester   Zahnarzt

Schauspieler   Polizistin

Friseur   Ingenieurin

Mechanikerin   Lehrerin

Male	Female
Friseur	

Q4 If you can get these right, you know it's sunk in. Write down the German for these job titles. Write down the version for a man or a woman, depending on what's in the brackets.

a) hairdresser *(man)*

....

b) builder *(woman)*

....

c) secretary *(woman)*

....

d) dentist *(man)*

....

e) policewoman

....

f) secretary *(man)*

....

g) engineer *(woman)*

....

h) actor *(man)*

....

i) teacher *(woman)*

....

Talking about Jobs

Q1 Draw lines to match the German on the left to the English on the right.

Ich bin Arzt	My friend George is an engineer
Mein Vater ist Mechaniker	My father is a mechanic
Meine Mutter ist Verkäuferin	I am a doctor
Mein Freund George ist Ingenieur	My mother is a salesperson
Ich arbeite bei Kwik Save	I have a part-time job
Ich habe einen Teilzeitjob	I work in Kwik Save

Q2 Write these out in English:

a) Ich möchte Sport lernen.

....

b) Ich möchte Zahnarzt werden.

....

c) Ich möchte Deutsch lernen, weil es einfach ist.

....

d) Ich möchte Mathe lernen, weil ich Lehrerin werden möchte.

....

e) Ich möchte Schauspieler werden, weil sie viel Geld verdienen.

....

Dear Mum, I want to be a scientist because you get to play with colourful chemicals and say mwah-ha-ha-ha at the end of every sentence...mwah-ha-ha-ha.

Q3 Finish off these sentences, using the phrases in the box.
The bits in brackets tell you what they should say.

a) Ich möchte Kunst lernen, weil .... (it's easy)

b) Ich möchte Arzt werden, weil .... (they earn a lot of money)

c) Ich möchte Mathe lernen, weil .... (I want to be a teacher)

d) Ich möchte Musik lernen, weil .... (it's fun)

> sie einfach ist   sie viel Geld verdienen
>
> sie lustig ist   ich Lehrer werden möchte

Ich möchte Deutsch studieren — honest...

It's a shame there's not more room, I was going to tell you about a job I had making moon cheese.

Directions

Q1 Here are some expressions you're bound to use when giving directions in German. Write down what they mean in English.

a) Nehmen Sie die zweite Straße links. ....

b) Nehmen Sie die dritte Straße rechts. ....

c) Gehen Sie rechts. ....

d) Gehen Sie links. ....

e) Gehen Sie geradeaus. ....

Ar, haha, ha-ha-ha, ar-ha-ha, ar-ar-ar, ar ha, 'tis mine!

Q2 Imagine you're working at a tourist office in Germany. Using the map, give the right directions to people asking these questions. The vocabulary in the map's key is there to help you.

a) Wo ist das Kino, bitte?

....

....

b) Gibt es hier in der Nähe eine Post?

....

....

c) Gibt es hier in der Nähe einen Bahnhof?

....

Map

Hotel Elite

Hotel Max

Hotel Zur Sonne

Key

▫ Post

🚂 Bahnhof

☠ Kino

🏛 Museum

ⓘ Verkehrsbüro

〰 Schwimmbad

Scale 0 km — 1 km

d) Wo ist das Museum, bitte?

....

e) Gibt es hier in der Nähe ein Schwimmbad?

....

Q3 Now you're at the **train station**. Lots of tourists need your help. Use the map from Q2 to give them directions and answer their questions in German.

HINT: Don't worry about working out the exact distances in kilometres.
Just check the scale of the map and estimate to the nearest km in your answers.

a) Wie weit ist die Post von hier?

....

b) Wie weit ist das Hotel Max von hier?

....

c) Wie weit ist das Kino von hier?

....

Shops

Q1 Answer these questions by choosing the right German shop from the blob. I've done the first one for you.

a) Your friends want to buy some local cheeses, sausages and other stuff. Where are you going to take them?

der Markt

b) Miss Lewis is desperate for chocolate. Where's the best place for her to get some?

c) Where can you buy a book?

d) It's Mr Jones' birthday. He's not very popular, so he wants to buy himself a birthday cake. Where will he get one?

e) It's Mr Brown's dog's birthday. Mr Brown wants to buy her a steak as a present. Where will he get one?

f) Where will you go to buy some fruit?

g) Thinking about shops gives you a headache. Where could you buy some tablets?

h) Where's your best bet for buying some bread?

der Markt die Metzgerei die Buchhandlung der Lebensmittelladen die Apotheke die Konditorei das Süßwarengeschäft die Bäckerei

Q2 Read these conversations and then answer the questions in English.

Hans: *Wo ist die Apotheke, bitte?*
Karl: *Gehen Sie links. Nehmen Sie die dritte Straße rechts.*
Hans: *Und wie weit ist sie von hier?*
Karl: *Sie ist ein Kilometer von hier.*
Hans: *Danke.*

a) What is Hans looking for? ....

b) How far away is it? ....

c) Which street should Hans take after he's turned left?
....

d) Where does Claudia want to go? ....

e) How far away is it? ....

f) Should Claudia turn left or right first of all? ....

Claudia: *Gibt es hier in der Nähe eine Buchhandlung?*
Karl: *Ja. Gehen Sie links. Nehmen Sie die erste Straße rechts. Es ist zwei Kilometer von hier.*
Claudia: *Danke.*
Karl: *Bitte sehr.*

Section 4 — Town, Shopping, Food and Drink

Places in Town

Q1 Here are two lists of place names. Draw lines to match the German words on the left to the English words on the right. I've done the first one for you.

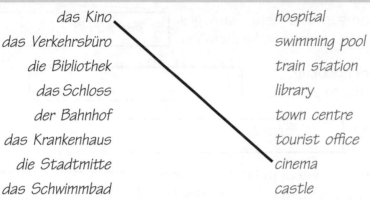

das Kino — cinema
das Verkehrsbüro — hospital
die Bibliothek — swimming pool
das Schloss — train station
der Bahnhof — library
das Krankenhaus — town centre
die Stadtmitte — tourist office
das Schwimmbad — castle

Ich habe das Schloss verloren.

Q2 Read this conversation, then answer the questions in English.

Sophie: Wo ist die Kirche?
Michael: Gehen Sie rechts.
Sophie: Und wo ist das Schloss, bitte?
Michael: Gehen Sie geradeaus. Nehmen Sie die zweite Straße links.
Sophie: Wie weit ist es von hier?
Michael: Es ist fünf Kilometer von hier.
Sophie: Und gibt es hier in der Nähe eine Buchhandlung?
Michael: Nein. Es gibt hier in der Nähe eine Bibliothek. Sie ist ein Kilometer von hier.
Sophie: Danke.

a) Where does Sophie want to go first?
....
b) To get to the castle, what must Sophie do?
....
....
c) How far away is the castle?
....
d) Is there a bookshop near the tourist office?
....
e) How far away is the library?
....

Q3 Now it's your turn to give the woman at the tourist office a hard time. Fill in your parts of the conversation below. The bits in brackets tell you what to say.

a) You: .... *[Where's the town hall, please?]*

Dagmar: Es ist in der Nähe von hier. Gehen Sie geradeaus. Nehmen Sie die dritte Straße rechts.

b) You: .... *[Where's the post office, please?]*

Dagmar: Gehen Sie links.

c) You: .... *[How far is it from here?]*

Dagmar: Es ist ein Kilometer von hier.

d) You: .... *[Is there a leisure centre near here?]*

Dagmar: Ja. Es ist zwei Kilometer von hier. Gehen Sie rechts. Nehmen Sie die erste Straße links.

e) You: .... *[Thanks.]*

Food and Drink

Q1 Here are some items of food in English. Write down what they are in German.

a) lamb ....

d) beef ....

b) seafood ....

e) ham ....

c) pork ....

f) chicken ....

Q2 Write these shopping lists out in English. Don't forget the titles.

ooooooooooooooo
SUPERMARKT ....

eine Wurst ....

Fisch ....

Steak ....

Pilze ....

ein Blumenkohl ....

vier Kartoffeln ....

ein Kohl ....

ein Kopfsalat ....

fünf Karotten ....

ooooooooooooooo
LEBENSMITTELLADEN ....

zwei Zitronen ....

eine Birne ....

ein Apfel ....

eine Zwiebel ....

Erbsen ....

drei Pfirsiche ....

eine Banane ....

vier Orangen ....

Q3 Mmm, pizza. Write the pizza toppings (and the salad bits) out in English.

HINT:
Some of the words are plurals. Look at the word endings.

PIZZA

Margherita

Tomaten ....

Prosciutto

Tomaten ....

Schinken ....

Pilze ....

Ai Funghi

Tomaten ....

Pilze ....

Zwiebeln ....

SALAT

Tomaten ....

Kopfsalat ....

Tomatensalat

Karotten ....

Zwiebeln ....

Obstsalat

Äpfel ....

Erdbeeren ....

Orangen ....

Q4 Which of the pizzas from Q3 would **not** be suitable for a vegetarian? ....

Food and Drink

Q1   Read through this restaurant drinks list and answer the questions below.

Apfelsaft	Cola	Bier	Weißwein	Kaffee
Orangensaft	Mineralwasser	Rotwein	heiße Schokolade	Tee

a)   Using the drinks list above, write the names of these drinks in German.

coffee ....   hot chocolate ....

mineral water ....   coke ....

orange juice ....

b)   Write down the five other words from the drinks list and what they mean in English.

....

....

Q2   Write the names of these foods in German.
Remember to write "der", "die" or "das" in front of each one.

a) ....   e) ....

b) ....   f) ....

c) ....   g) ....

d) ....   h) ....

Q3   Look at these lists of food and drink. Which one is the odd one out in each list, and why? I've done the first one for you.

Hint: There may be more than one way to say which is the odd one out. Just put down the one you think is most obvious.

a) Milch, Mineralwasser, Eis, Tee   *Eis, because ice cream isn't a drink.* ....

b) Kartoffelchips, Kuchen, Zucker, Schokolade...

c) Joghurt, Sahne, Getreideflocken, Butter ....

d) Rotwein, Milch, Bier, Weißwein ....

e) Tee, Kaffee, heiße Schokolade, Cola ....

f) Heiße Schokolade, Mineralwasser, Orangensaft ....

g) Pommes frites, Reis, Brot, Suppe ....

Food and Drink

Q1   How would you say these things in German?

a) Are you thirsty?

....

b) I don't like chocolate.

....

c) I'm hungry.

....

d) I don't like jam.

....

e) I'm not thirsty.

....

f) I like milk.

....

Q2   Read about Lisa's eating habits then answer the questions in English.

> Das Frühstück ist um sieben Uhr.
> Ich esse Getreideflocken und trinke Kaffee.
>
> Das Mittagessen ist um ein Uhr.
> Ich esse Schweinefleisch und Reis.
> Ich trinke Cola.
>
> Das Abendessen ist um acht Uhr. Ich
> esse Hähnchen und Nudeln. Ich trinke
> Weißwein.
>
> Lisa

a) What time does Lisa eat breakfast?

....

b) What does Lisa have for breakfast?

....

c) What does Lisa eat and drink at lunchtime?

....

d) What time does Lisa eat lunch?

....

e) What does Lisa eat and drink for dinner?

....

Q3   Dominik is interviewing Frau Meyer about mealtimes at her guesthouse and her eating habits. Complete their conversation about mealtimes. The bits in brackets tell you what to say.

Dominik: *Um wie viel Uhr ist das Frühstück, Frau Meyer?*

a) Frau Meyer: .... *[It's at 6 o'clock.]*

Dominik: *Was essen Sie?*

b) Frau Meyer: .... *[I eat bread. I drink tea.]*

Dominik: *Was trinken Sie?*

c) Frau Meyer: .... *[I drink mineral water.]*

Alas, no doughnuts...

You don't need to know "doughnuts" for KS3 German. And you don't need to know about J. F. Kennedy's famous speech where they reckon he said "I'm a jam doughnut". So stop reading this and do the questions.

Food and Drink

Q1   Draw lines to match the German words to the English words. I've done the first one for you.

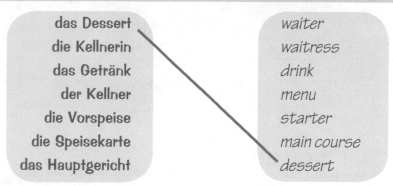

das Dessert
die Kellnerin
das Getränk
der Kellner
die Vorspeise
die Speisekarte
das Hauptgericht

waiter
waitress
drink
menu
starter
main course
dessert

Q2   You're at a restaurant. Use the menu to help you fill in your parts of this conversation in German. The bits in brackets tell you what to say.

Hint:
welche = which
Salat = salad

Kellner: *Guten Abend.*

a) You: ....
   [A table for one please.]

Kellner: *Was möchten Sie trinken?*

b) You: .... *[I'd like a beer.]*

Kellner: *Welche Vorspeise möchten Sie?*

c) You: .... *[I'd like the soup.]*

Kellner: *Und das Hauptgericht?*

d) You: ....
   [Do you have lamb?]

Kellner: *Ja!*

e) You: ....
   [I'd like lamb, potatoes and peas.]

Menu

VORSPEISE
Suppe   Salat

HAUPTGERICHT
Hähnchen   Lammfleisch
Rindfleisch Schweinefleisch
Nudeln   Reis
Kartoffeln   Erbsen
Karotten

DESSERT
Kuchen   Eis

Q3   What's the German for these phrases? Choose the right phrase from the box.

a) I'd like to reserve a table.

....

....

Ich hätte gern Tisch.
Ich möchte einen reservieren Tisch.
Ich möchte einen Tisch reservieren.

b) I'd like cabbage.

....

....

Ich hätte gern Kopfsalat.
Ich hätte gern Kohl.
Ich hätte gern Blumenkohl.

Q4   How do you tell the waiter you want to pay, in German?

....

Clothes and Colours

Q1 Write down the German name for these items of clothing.
Don't forget to write "der", "die" or "das". I've done the first one for you.

a) ....*der Mantel*........

e) ....

b) ....

f) ....

c) ....

g) ....

d) ....

h) ....

Q2 Write these sentences out in English.

a) Ich trage einen blauen Pullover. *I'm wearing a blue jumper.*.............

b) Frau Becker trägt einen rosa Regenmantel. ....

c) Tobias trägt eine grüne Hose. ....

d) Anna trägt einen weißen Rock. ....

e) Mein Vater trägt einen grauen Hut. ....

f) Sophie trägt ein orange T-Shirt. ....

g) Sie trägt eine gelbe Bluse. ....

h) Er trägt eine rote Krawatte. ....

Be this groovy,
learn some German.

Q3 Describe what these people are wearing, in German. Don't forget to mention the colours.

a)

yellow ....

....

....

blue ....

....

black ....

b)

green

brown

....

....

....

Clothes and Colours

Q1 Write these phrases out in English. Choose from the English phrases in the box.

a) Sonst noch etwas? ....

b) Ich lasse es. ....

c) Das kostet zehn Euro. ....

d) Ich nehme das. ....

e) Ich möchte eine Hose. ....

f) Was kostet das? ....

g) Haben Sie einen Regenmantel? ....

....

It's 10 euros.

I'll take that one.

I'll leave it.

How much is that?

Do you have a raincoat?

Anything else?

I'd like a pair of trousers.

Q2 You want to buy presents for two of your friends. You've decided to buy them both clothes. Fill in your parts of these two conversations. The bits in brackets tell you what to say.

a) You: ....

[Do you have a yellow T-shirt?]

Die Verkäuferin: *Ich habe nur ein orange T-Shirt und ein rotes T-Shirt.*

b) You: ....

[I'll leave it.]

Die Verkäuferin: *Sonst noch etwas?*

c) You: ....

[Yes please. I would like a yellow hat.]

Die Verkäuferin: *Das kostet zehn Euro.*

d) You: ....

[I'll take that one. Thank you.]

Die Verkäuferin: *Bitte sehr.*

e) You: ....

[Do you have a woollen jumper?]

Der Verkäufer: *Ja. Möchten Sie einen schwarzen Wollpullover?*

f) You: ....

[No thank you, I'd like a blue jumper.]

Der Verkäufer: *Hätten Sie diesen Pullover gern?*

g) You: ....

[Yes, I'll take that one.]

Der Verkäufer: *Sonst noch einen Wunsch?*

h) You: ....

[No thank you. How much is that?]

Der Verkäufer: *Zwanzig Euro neunzig Cent.*

Sports and Musical Instruments

Q1 Write out the names of these sports, in German.

a) football   ....

b) badminton   ....

c) rugby   ....

d) table tennis   ....

e) chess   ....

f) tennis   ....

g) cricket   ....

For those watching in black and white, the pink is the one next to the blue.

Q2 I paid the temping agency peanuts, so they sent a monkey to do my typing. I told it to write out some musical instruments in German, but it got the letters in the wrong order. Write the letters out in the correct order.

a) edi   etrraig   ....

b) ide   rmepteo   ....

c) sad   velakri   ....

d) eid   klaietetnr   ....

e) ads   lolec   ....

f) dei   eggie   ....

g) sad guezgalhcs   ....

Secrets of Publishing #467: Expert typesetters in action.

Q3 The words in these sentences are in the wrong order. Write them in the correct order.

a) spiele Kricket und Schach ich Trompete

....

b) ich Klavier Geige und Federball spiele

....

c) Fußball spiele Tennis und spiele ich Schlagzeug und ich

....

d) Schach Tischtennis und Klarinette spiele ich

....

e) Cello Kricket Geige ich und spiele

....

Pastimes and Hobbies

Q1   Complete these German sentences about hobbies.

a) Ich .... Rad.   d) Ich .... kegeln.

b) Ich .... wandern.   e) Ich .... einkaufen.

c) Ich ....

Q2   These sentences are wrong. Write them out properly. I've done the first one for you.

a) Ich kegeln gehe.   *Ich gehe kegeln.* ....

b) Ich gehen wandern.   ....

c) Ich fahre einkaufen.   ....

d) Ich fahre Schlittschuh. ....

e) Ich Rad fahre.   ....

Q3   Write these opinions out in words, in German. I've done the first one for you.

KEY
☺ = like
☺☺ = love
☹ = don't like
☹☹ = hate

a) ☺ + football   *Ich mag Fußball.* ....

b) ☺☺ + badminton ....

c) ☹ + chess   ....

d) ☹☹ + tennis   ....

e) ☺ + cricket   ....

Q4   Put these reasons into German for the sentences above.
I've done the first one for you so you can see what I mean.

a) because it is fantastic   *, weil es fantastisch ist* ....

b) because it is easy   ....

c) because it is boring   ....

d) because it is tiring   ....

e) because it is interesting   ....

TV, Books and Radio

Q1   What do these sentences mean in English?

a) Ich höre Musik.

....

c) Ich sehe mir Filme an.

....

b) Ich lese Zeitschriften.

....

d) Ich lese Romane.

....

Q2   Write German sentences, saying you like or dislike reading, listening to or watching the following things. ☺ = like, ☹ = dislike.

a) ☺   Romane   ....

b) ☹   Radio   ....

c) ☺   fernsehen   ....

d) ☹   Zeitungen   ....

e) ☺   Bücher   ....

Q3   Rewrite the sentences in question 1 to say:

a) I like this music.   *Ich mag diese Musik.*

b) I like this film.   ....

c) I like this magazine.   ....

d) I like this newspaper.   ....

Q4   Karin has written her diary for the day. Read what she has written, then answer the questions.

Montag: Ich sehe fern aber ich mag diesen Film nicht.
Ich lese auch Zeitschriften und Zeitungen.
Ich spiele Geige aber nicht Rugby! Ich gehe gern einkaufen und wandern.

a) What two things does she say she reads?

....

b) What musical instrument does she play?

....

c) What does she say about shopping?

....

Second oldest joke in the world...

Don't mix up your "Zeitschriften" and your "Zeitungen". Don't forget it's "Musik" with a "k".
Don't forget the "an" from "ich sehe Filme an". And don't forget to... oh dear, I've forgotten. HA HA.

Going Out and Making Arrangements

Q1   Write down **in German** where you'd go to do each of these things.
       All the words you need are in the box. The first one's done for you.

a)   See all the sights and do a bit of shopping

die Stadtmitte ....

b)   Go for a workout or a game of squash

....

c)   Watch a film

....

d)   Improve your doggy paddle

....

e)   Go for dinner

....

f)   See a play

....

g)   Watch telly and have a nice cup of tea

....

> nach Hause   das Kino
> die Stadtmitte   das Theater   das Restaurant
> das Schwimmbad   das Freizeitzentrum

Q2   The sentences in a) to f) could all be used to answer the question below.
       Finish them off with the right German word from the oval.

Hast du Lust ins Restaurant zu gehen?

a) Ja, ... **Yes, OK.**

b) Nein, ... **No, thank you.**

c) Ich habe kein .... **I don't have any money.**

d) Ja, das .... schön. **Yes, I'd love to.**

e) Ich mache meine .... **I'm doing my homework.**

f) Ich .... nicht gern ins Restaurant. **I don't like going to restaurants.**

> gehe
> danke
> Geld
> Hausaufgaben
> gerne
> wäre

Q3   Fill in the missing bits of these conversations **in German**.

a) You: ....
                [Do you want to go to the swimming pool?]

    Charlotte: Ja, gute Idee.

b) You: ....
                [Do you want to go to the cinema?]

    Sabine: Ja, das wäre schön.

c) You: ....
                [Do you want to go to the town centre?]

    Werner: Ja, gerne.

Going Out and Making Arrangements

Q1 Here are some answers to the question **"Wann treffen wir uns?"**
Draw lines to match the German on the left with the English on the right.

Treffen wir uns morgen.	Let's meet at 9 o'clock (am).
Treffen wir uns um neun Uhr.	Let's meet at 9 o'clock (pm).
Treffen wir uns heute Abend.	Let's meet on Saturday.
Treffen wir uns um einundzwanzig Uhr.	Let's meet this evening.
Treffen wir uns morgen früh.	Let's meet tomorrow.
Treffen wir uns am Sonnabend.	Let's meet tomorrow morning.

Q2 These are all useful sentences for saying **where** you're going to meet. Fill in the missing words.

a) Treffen wir uns vor .... Museum.

b) Treffen wir uns .... Restaurant.

c) Treffen wir uns bei mir ....

d) Treffen wir .... im Park.

e) Treffen wir uns vor .... Bank.

> Remember AFTER "VOR" —
> use "dem" for "der" and "das" words, and "der" for "die" words.

Q3 Fill in the missing bits of this conversation about arranging to go to the cinema, **in German**.

You: ....
[Do you want to go to the cinema?]

Dieter: *Ja, das wäre schön. Wann treffen wir uns?*

You: ....
[Let's meet at seven o'clock (pm).]

Sophie: *Ja, gerne. Und wo?*

You: ....
[Let's meet in front of the tourist office.]

Q4 This conversation will get you some tickets. Translate the missing bits into German.

You: ....
[How much does a ticket cost, please?]

Verkäuferin: *Eine Karte kostet fünf Euro.*

You: ....
[I would like four tickets, please.]

Verkäuferin: *Zwanzig Euro.*

You: ....
[Thank you.]

Transport

Q1 Write down the names of these vehicles in German.
Don't forget the der, die or das.

a)

....

b)

....

c)

....

d)

....

Q2 Write these vehicles names out in English.

a) der Reisebus

....

b) die U-Bahn

....

c) das Schiff

....

d) die Straßenbahn

....

e) der Zug

....

f) der Bus

....

Q3 For each of these, write a sentence to say that's how
you travel. I've done the first one for you.

a) *Ich fahre mit dem Bus.* ....

b) ....

c) ....

d) ....

e) ....

f) ....

Transport

Q1   Here are Lisa's travel plans for the next week.
For each day, write down **where** she's going, and **how**.

a) *Montag* Ich fahre mit dem Auto nach Mainz.   ....

b) *Dienstag* Ich gehe zu Fuß nach Bonn.   ....

c) *Mittwoch* Ich fahre mit dem Fahrrad zur Schule. ....

d) *Donnerstag* Ich fahre mit dem Reisebus nach Italien. ....

e) *Freitag* Ich reise mit dem Flugzeug nach Frankreich. ....

Q2   What sort of tickets do you want to buy? Write the
answers in German. I've done the first one for you.

HINT: The plural of "Karte" is "Karten".

a) 2 × ⇦⇨, Ist *Zwei Rückfahrkarten, erster Klasse.* ....

b) 3 × ⇨, 2nd ....

c) 1 × ⇦⇨, 2nd ....

d) 4 × ⇨, 1st ....

e) 2 × ⇦⇨, 2nd ....

Q3   Suzanne asks the following questions at the ticket office.
Write down what they mean in English.

a) Wann fährt der Zug nach Mannheim?

....

b) Von welchem Gleis fährt der Zug ab?

....

This cycling lark doesn't seem to be getting me very far.

c) Fährt ein Zug nach Hamburg?

....

Q4   Imagine you are the official in the ticket office. Answer Suzanne's questions,
in German, in full. The bits in brackets give you a clue what to say.

a) *[18:00]* ....

b) *[12]* ....

c) *[✓]* ....

Post Office and Telephones

Q1 Match these descriptions to the most appropriate German words in the box. I've done the first one for you.

a) Write this on your letter, or they won't know where to send it. ...die Adresse...

b) It's not a card, but you do put this in an envelope. ....

c) When you want to post something, you put it in here. ....

d) You'll need to buy one of these if you want your letter to go anywhere. ....

e) You usually send somebody one of these when you are on holiday. ....

eine Briefmarke   eine Postkarte   ein Briefkasten   die Adresse   ein Brief

Q2 Read these two post office conversations, and answer the questions in English.

HINT:
der Postbeamter =
post office worker

Maria:	Ich möchte diesen Brief nach Österreich schicken. Was kostet es?
Postbeamter:	Es kostet ein Euro zwölf Cent. Sonst noch etwas?
Maria:	Ja. Ich möchte eine Ein-Euro-Briefmarke, bitte.
Postbeamter:	Zwei Euro zwölf Cent, bitte.
Maria:	Danke.

Paul:	Ich möchte eine Drei-Euro-Briefmarke, bitte.
Postbeamter:	Sonst noch etwas?
Paul:	Ja. Ich möchte eine Postkarte nach Frankreich schicken. Was kostet es?
Postbeamter:	Es kostet einundfünfzig Cent. Drei Euro einundfünfzig Cent, bitte.
Paul:	Danke.

a) How much will it cost Maria to send her letter? ....

b) To which country is Maria sending her letter? ....

c) What else does she want? ....

d) What is Paul sending to France? ....

e) How much will this one item cost? ....

f) What else does Paul want? ....

Q3 Fill in your parts of this phone conversation, in German. The bits in brackets tell you what to say.

Frau Schulz: Hallo.

a)   You: ....
[Hello. It's (your name) here. Can I speak to Katharina, please?]

Frau Schulz: Sie ist nicht hier.

b)   You: ....
[Where is she, please?]

Frau Schulz: Sie ist in der Bibliothek. Was ist Ihre Telefonnummer?

c)   You: ....
[My telephone number is 763715. Thanks, Mrs Schulz.]

Informal Letters

Q1   Write out these informal letter phrases in English. Choose from the phrases in the blob.

    a)   Vielen Dank für deinen Brief. ....

    b)   Viele Grüße. ....

    c)   Schreib bald. ....

    d)   Bis bald. ....

    e)   Wie geht's? ....

> Best wishes.   How are you?
> See you soon.   Write soon.
> Thanks for your letter.

Q2   Read this letter, then answer the questions (in **English**).

> Wien, den 20. Mai
>
> Liebe Sam,
>
> ich habe mich so gefreut, mal wieder von dir zu hören.
>
> Was ist dein Lieblingsfach? Mein Lieblingsfach ist Kunst, weil sie einfach ist. Ich hasse Naturwissenschaften, weil sie langweilig und schwierig sind. Welches Schulfach hasst du?
>
> Schreib bald!
>
> **Lukas**

    a)   Is Sam a boy or a girl?

    ....

    b)   What is the first thing Lukas says, after the "Liebe Sam" bit?

    ....

    c)   Why does Lukas hate science?

    ....

    d)   What does Lukas tell Sam to do at the end of his letter?

    ....

Q3   Imagine you're Lukas's penfriend, Sam. Write an informal reply in German to his letter in Q2. Include all the information given below.

HINT: Use the letter in Q2 to help you.

- Sam (i.e. you) lives in Manchester.
- The date is 1st June.
- Thank Lukas for his letter.
- Ask him how he is.
- Your favourite subject is history because it's interesting.
- Finish the letter with "Best wishes" and sign the letter "Sam".

....
....
....
....
....
....
....
....

Formal Letters

Q1   Use a word from inside the circle to complete these special phrases from formal letters.

a) Mit .... Grüßen

b) .... Dank .... Voraus

c) Sehr .... Damen und Herren

d) Sehr .... Herr Werner

> im   vielen
> geehrter   geehrte
> freundlichen

Q2   Read Linda's letter to Mrs Fischer at Pension Fischer and answer the questions.

> *Linda Foster*
> *Puddle Lane*
> *Gloucester*
> *Gloucestershire GL1 5RH*
> *Großbrittanien*
> *Gloucester, den 13.01.2013*
>
> *Sehr geehrte Frau Fischer,*
>
> *wenn möglich, möchte ich bei Ihnen ein Einzelzimmer reservieren, vom 8. bis zum 15. März. Könnten Sie mich bitte informieren, wie viel es kosten wird?*
>
> *Vielen Dank im Voraus,*
>
> *Linda Foster*

a) If Linda had to write to
    Mr Fischer instead of Mrs Fischer,
    how would she start this letter?

    ....

b) How would you start a letter like this
    if you didn't know the person's name?

    ....

c) What does "Vielen Dank im Voraus" mean?

    ....

Q3   Write a formal letter in German, using the information given
     below and your own name and address. Use today's date.

- You're writing to Mr Neumann at Hotel Dieter.

- Say you'd like to reserve a double room from the 23rd of October to the 28th of October.

- Ask how much it will cost.

- Say "Many thanks in advance".

- Put "Yours sincerely" and your name.

Weather and Seasons

Q1 Here you have pictures describing what the weather's like. Choose from the phrases in the box the appropriate phrase to label the picture

a) ....

b) ....

c) ....

d) ....

es ist heiss
es ist windig   es ist sonning
es ist schlecht   es ist kalt

Q2 Our typist has made some mistakes and the letters in these words have got mixed up. Unscramble the letters and write the words out — they're all answers to the question "Wie ist das Wetter?". I've done the first one for you.

a) se tis chchtles *Es ist schlecht.* ....

b) se tis webkltö ....

c) se gnteer ....

d) se its nnigos ....

e) es sit altk ....

f) se sti gidwin ....

g) se its tug ....

h) se chnesti ....

Q3 Here are two lists of seasons. Draw lines to match up the German and the English.

der Sommer
der Winter
der Frühling
der Herbst

Spring
Winter
Summer
Autumn

There must be more to life than this...

Fig 41.1: The Evolution of Man

Q4 Write these out in German.

a) It's snowing.

....

b) What's the weather like?

....

c) It's bad weather.

....

d) It's stormy.

....

'Tis an ill wind that blows no good — eh?...

There's a <u>handy trick</u> for remembering your seasons. "<u>der Sommer</u>" and "<u>der Winter</u>" are <u>easy</u>. "<u>der Frühling</u>" and "<u>der Herbst</u>" are trickier — but remember, "<u>Frühling</u>" rhymes with "<u>spring</u>".

Holidays

Q1　Here are some questions you might be asked about holidays. You might even want to use them yourself if you're nosy. Draw lines to match the German with the right English translations.

Mit wem fährst du in Urlaub?	How long do you go on holiday for?
Wie ist das Wetter normalerweise?	What do you do?
Wo übernachtest du normalerweise?	What's the weather like normally?
Wohin fährst du normalerweise in Urlaub?	Where do you go on holiday normally?
Was machst du?	Where do you normally stay?
Wie lange machst du Urlaub?	Who do you go on holiday with?

Q2　Read this conversation and then answer the questions in English.

Claudia:　Wohin fährst du normalerweise in Urlaub, Michael?
Michael:　Normalerweise fahre ich nach Spanien. Und du?
Claudia:　Normalerweise fahre ich nach England.
Michael:　Wie ist das Wetter normalerweise?
Claudia:　Es regnet. Was machst du in Spanien?
Michael:　Ich gehe an den Strand und ich schwimme.
Claudia:　Wie lange machst du Urlaub?
Michael:　Ich mache zehn Tage Urlaub. Ich übernachte in einem Hotel.

a)　Where does Michael normally go on holiday?　.............................

b)　What's the weather normally like in England according to Claudia?　.............................

c)　Name one thing Michael does when he's on holiday.　.............................

d)　How long does Michael go on holiday for?　.............................

e)　Where does he normally stay?　.............................

Q3　Fill in your bits of this conversation about holidays **in German**.

Karl:　*Wohin fährst du normalerweise in Urlaub?*

You:　..
　　　　　　　　　　　　　　　　　　　　　　　Normally I go to France.]

Karl:　*Mit wem fährst du?*

You:　..
　　　　　　　　　　　　　　　　　　　　　　　[I go with my aunt.]

Karl:　*Wo übernachtest du normalerweise?*

You:　..
　　　　　　　　　　　　　　　　　　　　　　　[I stay in a youth hostel.]

Section 7 — Weather, Holidays and Countries

Hotels and Camping

Q1 These are words that you will need about hotels, hostels and camping. For each one, draw a (ring) round the correct English meaning:

a) *der Campingplatz* = campsite // youth hostel

b) *die Jugendherberge* = campsite // youth hostel

c) *der Platz* = pitch (space for a tent) // tent

d) *der Wohnwagen* = caravan // drinking water

e) *der Schlafsack* = sleeping bag // tent

f) *das Trinkwasser* = drinking water // tent

Q2 Here are some words you will need in a hotel but the vowels have gone missing. Write them out, filling in the missing letters. I've done the first one for you:

a) d...r   Sp... ...s...s... ...l   *der Speisesaal*

b) d... ...   T... ...l...tt...   ....

c) d...s   T...l...f...n   ....

d) ... ... n   Z...mm...r   ....

e) D...sch...   ....

f) B...lk...n   ....

g) B...d   ....

Now that's more like it, yeah baby

Fig 43.1: Why CGP Airlines went bust.

Q3 Write down, in German, how you would describe these rooms. I've done the first one for you.

a) *Ein Einzelzimmer mit Balkon.*

b) ....

c) ....

d) ....

e) ....

44

Booking Accommodation

Q1 Here are some questions you use to book a hotel room. Draw lines to match the German on the left to the English on the right. I've done the first one for you.

German	English
Haben Sie Zimmer frei?	How much is that?
Ich möchte hier zwei Nächte bleiben.	How many nights?
Für wie viele Nächte?	I would like to stay from the 4th May to the 2nd June.
Was kostet das?	Have you any rooms free?
Ich möchte vom vierten Mai bis zum zweiten Juni bleiben.	I would like to stay two nights.

Q2 You are in a hotel in Germany. Fill in the missing parts of the conversation between you and the receptionist, in German. The bits in brackets tell you what to say.

HINT: Empfangschef = hotel receptionist

a) You: ....
[Have you any rooms free?]

Empfangschef: Ja. Für wie viele Personen?

b) You: ....
[I'd like a double room.]

Empfangschef: Für wie viele Nächte?

c) You: ....
[I would like to stay for 2 weeks. How much is that?]

Empfangschef: Das kostet €480.

Q3 Read the notes below, then answer the questions. Write "T" for true and "F" for false in the boxes.

a) Mick wants a double room ☐

b) Vicky wants to stay for two weeks. ☐

c) Gary want a single room ☐

d) Vicky wants a double room. ☐

e) Gary wants to stay one week. ☐

Ich möchte ein Doppelzimmer.
Ich möchte hier zwei Nächte bleiben.
Vicky

Ich möchte ein Einzelzimmer.
Ich möchte von ersten Mai
bis zum elften Juni bleiben.
Mick

Ich möchte ein Doppelzimmer.
Ich möchte hier eine Woche bleiben.
Gary

Countries

Q1   Look at the map. I've taken off the country names, and put on a), b), c) etc. On the left, write the name of the country that goes with each letter, **in German**. I've done the first one for you.

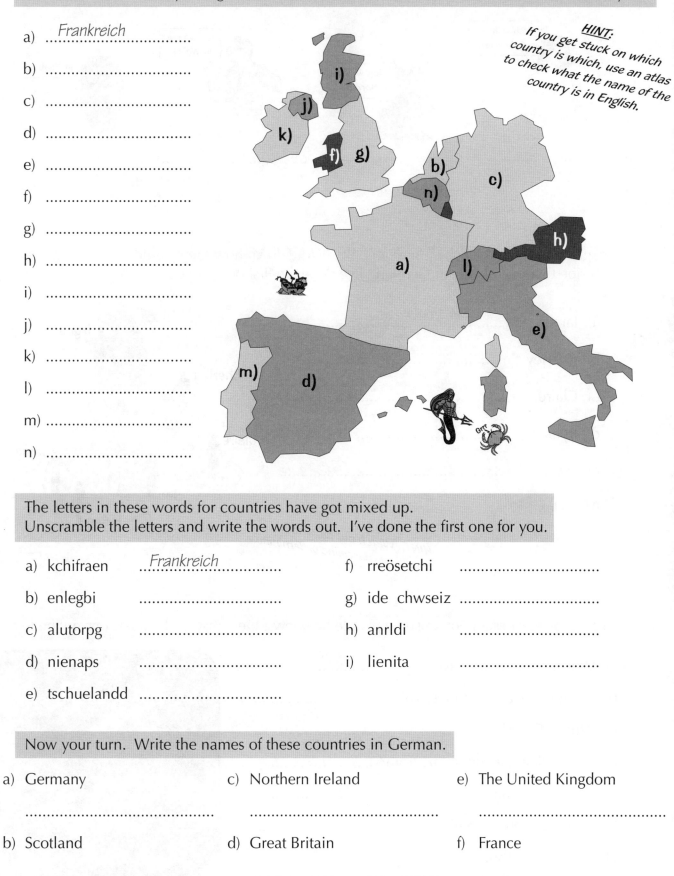

a)   *Frankreich* ....

b)   ....

c)   ....

d)   ....

e)   ....

f)   ....

g)   ....

h)   ....

i)   ....

j)   ....

k)   ....

l)   ....

m)   ....

n)   ....

HINT: If you get stuck on which country is which, use an atlas to check what the name of the country is in English.

Q2   The letters in these words for countries have got mixed up.
Unscramble the letters and write the words out. I've done the first one for you.

a) kchifraen   *Frankreich* ....   f) rreösetchi ....

b) enlegbi   ....   g) ide chwseiz ....

c) alutorpg   ....   h) anrldi ....

d) nienaps   ....   i) lienita ....

e) tschuelandd ....

Q3   Now your turn. Write the names of these countries in German.

a) Germany   c) Northern Ireland   e) The United Kingdom

....

b) Scotland   d) Great Britain   f) France

....

Section 7 — Weather, Holidays and Countries

Nationalities

Q1 Read what these people are saying in German, then write down where they come from, in English.

a) ....

b) ....

c) ....

d) ....

Q2 Imagine that you are each of these people. Write down how they would describe their nationality in German. I've done the first one for you.

a) James   *Ich bin Engländer.* ....

b) Charley ....

c) Claire ....

d) Iryna ....

e) Ian ....

f) Helen ....

HINT: Watch out for whether it should be masculine or feminine.

Iryna

Charley

Claire

James

Ian

Helen

Q3 Read Thomas's description of some people he knows, then answer the questions on the left.

a) Where does Thomas live? ....

b) What nationality is Vincenzo? ....

c) Who is English? ....

d) Where does Jacques come from? ....

e) Who is Spanish? ....

f) Where is Robert from? ....

g) Where does Paul live? ....

Ich bin Deutsche, und ich wohne in Deutschland. Jacques ist Franzose. Vincenzo ist Italiener, er wohnt in Italien. Lucy ist Engländerin und Pablo ist Spanier. Paul ist Waliser, aber wohnt in England. Robert ist Schotte.

Opinions

Q1   Write these sentences out in German.

a) I like tea. [tea = der Tee]

....

b) I love Maths. [Maths = die Mathe]

....

c) I don't like coffee. [coffee = Kaffee]

....

d) I hate goldfish.   [goldfish = die Goldfische]

....

e) I like German. [German = Deutsch]

....

f) I don't like science. [science = Naturwissenschaften]

....

Q2   Complete the following sentences with the right word from the box.
The bits on the right tell you what you need to say.

a)   Ich .... gern. *(I like swimming.)*

b)   .... esse gern Pizza. *(I like eating pizza.)*

c)   Ich schlafe .... *(I like sleeping.)*

Ich
gern
schwimme

Q3   Our typist has mixed up the letters in these words. Unscramble the letters and
write out the words. They're all describing words. I've done the first one for you.

a) wndrbarue   ....*wunderbar*....

b) lolt   ....

c) fdoo   ....

d) tischtasfan   ....

e) faceinh sselak   ....

f) dnegnertsna   ....

g) werchs   ....

h) ssntaeertin   ....

Q4   Write the following out in German. (Hint: history = Geschichte)

a) History is great.   ....

b) History is tiring.   ....

c) History is hard.   ....

d) History is good.   ....

e) History is fantastic.   ....

I think this page is the best page I've ever seen...

It's <u>weird</u> how you add "gern" to a sentence and suddenly it's talking about <u>liking</u>. That's because
"gern" means "<u>gladly</u>". So "Ich schwimme <u>gern</u>" = "I swim <u>gladly</u>" = "I <u>like</u> swimming". Amazing.

Asking Questions

Q1   Here are two lists of question words. Draw lines to
      match the English to the German words on either side.

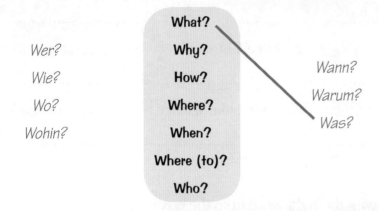

Wer?   **What?**
                         Why?   *Wann?*
Wie?   **How?**   *Warum?*
Wo?   **Where?**   *Was?*
                         When?
Wohin?   **Where (to)?**
                         Who?

Q2   Write in the best word from the circle to complete each question.
      Use each word once only. I've done the first one for you.

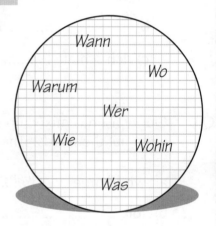

a) ......*Wer*......... ist Ihre Mutter? [... is your mother?]

b) .... fahren Sie? [... are you going?]

c) .... ist dein Geburtstag? [... is your birthday?]

d) .... sind meine Schuhe? [... are my shoes?]

e) .... magst du mich nicht? [... don't you like me?]

f) .... weit ist es von hier? [... far is it from here?]

g) .... möchten Sie? [... would you like?]

Q3   Here's a load of statements. Change them into simple yes/no questions.
      Then translate your questions into English. I've done the first one for you.

a) Du möchtest einen Apfel.
    [You would like an apple.]   *Möchtest du einen Apfel? (Would you like an apple?)*

b) Er heißt Romeo.
    [He is called Romeo.]   ....

c) Du hast einen Hund.
    [You have a dog.]   ....

d) Wir lernen Deutsch.
    [We learn German.]   ....

e) Es gibt hier in der Nähe ein Schloss.
    [There is a castle near here.] ....

Nouns — Capital Letters and Gender

Q1 Some of these words are nouns, and should be written with a capital letter. Find the nouns, and write them out correctly. Look them up in a dictionary if you're not sure.

ein   fußball   schuh   toll

katze   das   heißen

groß   zeit   die

der   freund

....

Q2 Write these nouns out in the correct boxes, depending on whether each is a der, die or das word (masculine, feminine or neuter). I've done the first one for you. HINT: They're all singular, not plural.

Pferd   Hund   Katze

Freundin

Schuh   Haus

Bruder   Kuli   Tante

~~Schwester~~   Onkel   Ohr

Cousine   Vater   Knie

DER (masculine)	DIE (feminine)	DAS (neuter)
	Schwester	

Q3 Draw lines to match up the singular words on the left, to their plurals on the right. I've done the first one for you.

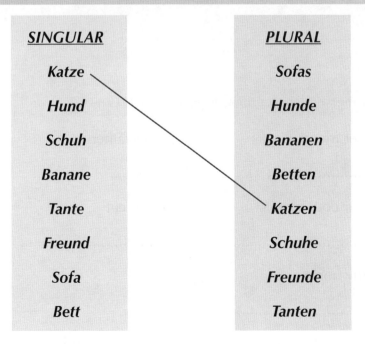

SINGULAR	PLURAL
Katze	Sofas
Hund	Hunde
Schuh	Bananen
Banane	Betten
Tante	Katzen
Freund	Schuhe
Sofa	Freunde
Bett	Tanten

...and then I drew a line from Katze to Katzen, and...

What a chump

How to Say 'A', & 'My' and 'Your'

Q1   Write these nouns out, adding the correct German word for "a" ("ein" or "eine"), depending on whether the word is masculine, feminine, or neuter. I've done the first one for you.

a) Katze

  eine Katze
....

b) Hund

....

c) Schuh

....

d) Banane

....

e) Tante

....

f) Cousin

....

g) Freund

....

h) Sofa

....

i) Bett

....

*HINT:
Check in a dictionary
if you're not sure
whether it's masc.,
fem. or neut.*

Q2   This time, write the nouns out adding the correct word for "my", depending on whether they are masculine, feminine or neuter. I've done the first one for you.

a) Pferd

  mein Pferd
....

b) Schuh

....

c) Kuli

....

d) Hund

....

e) Katze

....

f) Onkel

....

g) Schwester

....

h) Bruder

....

i) Vater

....

j) Freundin

....

k) Tante

....

l) Cousin

....

m) Haus

....

n) Ohr

....

o) Knie

....

Q3   Write these out in German. HINT: The words for dog, brother etc are all in Q1 and Q2.

a) my dog

....

b) their brother

....

c) my uncle

....

d) her friend (female)

....

e) our cousin (male)

....

f) my horse

....

g) his father

....

h) our cat

....

Pronouns — I, You, He, They

Q1   Draw lines to match up the German pronouns with the English ones.

sie   he

du   it

er   we

es   you (informal plural)

wir   they

ihr   she

Sie   you (informal singular)

Q2   Rewrite these phrases, replacing the underlined bits with the
appropriate pronoun (I, you, him…) I've done the first one for you.

a) <u>Miriam und Peter</u> trinken Wasser.
[Miriam and Peter drink water]

Sie trinken Wasser.

b) <u>Peter, Maria und ich</u> haben lange Haare.
[<u>Peter, Maria and I</u> have long hair.]

....

c) <u>Roger</u> ist hier. [<u>Roger</u> is here.]

....

d) <u>Meine Tante</u> kauft Brot. [<u>My aunt</u> buys bread.]

....

e) Wie alt ist <u>Peter</u>? [How old is <u>Peter</u>?]

....

Q3   Write these sentences again, replacing the underlined words
with one of the pronouns "sie","er" or "es". I've done the first one for you.

a) <u>Die Katze</u> ist süß.   *Sie ist süß.* ....

b) <u>Der Hund</u> ist groß.   ....

c) <u>Die Kuh</u> ist dumm.   ....

d) <u>Der Kuli</u> ist grün.   ....

e) <u>Das Pferd</u> ist schwarz.   ....

Section 8 — Grammar and Phrases

The Object (a.k.a. When to Use the Accusative Case)

Note: To save you looking them all up in the dictionary, I've put der, die or das in brackets after the words, to show you whether they'd normally be der, die or das words. They're all singular words — there aren't any plurals.

Q1 Write the accusative (object) form of these words out by putting "den", "die" or "das" in front of them. I've done the first one for you.

a) ....*den*.... Wagen [der]

b) .... Getränk [das]

c) .... Schwester [die]

d) .... Monat [der]

e) .... Maus [die]

f) .... Jahr [das]

g) .... Speisekarte [die]

h) .... Schloss [das]

i) .... Blumenkohl [der]

j) .... Kuh [die]

k) .... Brot [das]

l) .... Morgen [der]

m) .... Schildkröte [die]

n) .... Hemd [das]

o) .... Katze [die]

p) .... Hund [der]

q) .... Briefmarke [die]

r) .... Kleid [das]

s) .... Tag [der]

t) .... Pfirsich [der]

u) .... Bäckerei [die]

v) .... Vogel [der]

w) .... Kaninchen [das]

x) .... Pferd [das]

Q2 Write the accusative (object) form of these words out by putting the correct form of "ein", "mein" or "kein" in front of them. I've done three examples for you.

EIN/EINE

a) ....*einen*.... Handschuh [der]

b) .... Eis [das]

c) .... Keks [der]

d) .... Bluse [die]

e) .... Zwiebel [die]

f) .... T-Shirt [das]

MEINE/ MEINE

g) ....*mein*.... Frühstück [das]

h) .... Adresse [die]

i) .... Bruder [der]

j) .... Orange [die]

k) .... Mantel [der]

l) .... Ei [das]

KEIN/KEINE

m) ....*keine*.... Banane [die]

n) .... Steak [das]

o) .... Brille [die]

p) .... Postkarte [die]

q) .... Pullover [der]

r) .... Schinken [der]

Q3 Complete these sentences with the correct accusative (object) form of the word given in CAPITALS.

a) *EIN:* Er kauft .... Mineralwasser. [das]

b) *EIN:* Claudia backt .... Kuchen. [der]

c) *KEIN:* Ich habe .... Milch. [die]

d) *EIN:* Du möchtest .... Cola. [die]

e) *MEIN:* Ich trage .... Hut. [der]

f) *MEIN:* Sie hat .... Socke. [die]

g) *KEIN:* Ich mag .... Rindfleisch. [das]

h) *KEIN:* Andreas trägt .... Krawatte. [die]

The Dative Case

Note: To save you looking them all up in the dictionary, I've put der, die or das in brackets after the words, to show you whether they'd normally be der, die or das words. If it's a plural, I've put "die pl".

Q1 Write the dative form of these words out by putting "dem", "der" or "den" in front of them. I've done the first one for you.

a) ...*den*.... Pilzen [die pl]

b) .... Hotel [das]

c) .... Museum [das]

d) .... Hamster [der]

e) .... Reis [der]

f) .... Briefkasten [der]

g) .... Bahnhof [der]

h) .... Metzgerei [die]

i) .... Kartoffel [die]

j) .... Bank [die]

k) .... Hose [die]

l) .... Erbsen [die pl]

m) .... Krankenhaus [das]

n) .... Apfelsaft [der]

o) .... Tomate [die]

p) .... Kopfsalat [der]

q) .... Konditorei [die]

r) .... Rathaus [das]

Q2 Write the dative form of these words out by putting the correct form of "ein", "mein" or "kein" in front of them. I've done three examples for you.

EIN/EINE

a) ...*einem*.... Pfirsich [der]

b) .... Erdbeere [die]

c) .... Wagen [der]

d) .... Speisekarte [die]

e) .... Bier [das]

f) .... Kellner [der]

MEIN/ MEINE

g) ...*meiner*.... Maus [die]

h) .... Hemd [das]

i) .... Hund [der]

j) .... Karte [die]

k) .... Rock [der]

l) .... Stadt [die]

KEIN/KEINE

m) ...*keinem*.... Rotwein [der]

n) .... Theater [das]

o) .... Wurst [die]

p) .... Abendessen [das]

q) .... Joghurt [der]

Q3 Complete these sentences with the preposition in CAPITALS and the correct dative form of "der", "die" or "das".

a) *IN:* Ich wohne .... Stadt. [die]

b) *ZU:* Frau Weber geht .... Bäckerei. [die]

c) *AUF:* Der Kaffee ist .... Tisch. [der]

d) *ZU:* Wir fahren .... Schloss. [das]

e) *GEGENÜBER:*
Die Bibliothek ist .... Post. [die]

f) *VON:* Der Brief ist .... Frau. [die]

g) *IN:* Ist sie .... Kino? [das]

h) *MIT:* Ich fahre .... Familie. [die]

i) *AN:* Er ist .... Schule. [die]

*HINT: in + dem = im, an + dem = am,
zu + der = zur, zu + dem = zum.*

Yikes — them's two scary lookin' pages...

Come out from behind the sofa, they're **not** that bad. It's just good old grammar practice — do things <u>over and over</u>, and they'll <u>lodge in your brain</u>. Promise. Try it and see. Ah, go on.

Adjectives — Words to Describe Things

Q1 Choose a word from the circle to complete the following sentences.
The bits in brackets tell you what they should say.

   a) Mein Hemd ist .... *(My shirt is <u>yellow</u>)*

   b) Der Rock ist .... *(The skirt is <u>big</u>)*

   c) Die Jacken sind .... *(The jackets are <u>old</u>)*

   d) Die Erbsen sind .... *(The peas are <u>green</u>)*

   e) Die Kekse sind .... *(The biscuits are <u>good</u>)*

grün gut
gelb alt
groß

Q2 Finish off these sentences. This time they start with
"der", "die" or "das". Look back at question 1 to help you.

   a) Das .... Hemd. *(yellow)*

   b) Der .... Rock. *(big)*

   c) Die .... Jacke. *(old)*

   d) Die .... Erbse. *(green)*

   e) Der .... Kekse. *(good)*

Q3 Now the sentences start with "ein" or "eine". Fill in the gaps to finish them off.
HINT: Watch out for the endings of the words you write in.

   a) Ein .... Hemd. *(yellow)*

   b) Ein .... Rock. *(big)*

   c) Eine .... Jacke. *(old)*

   d) Eine .... Erbse. *(green)*

   e) Ein .... Keks. *(good)*

I'm wearing a yellow shirt... honest.

Q4 Write these sentences out in German.

   a) The green dress. *(dress = das Kleid)* ....

   b) A green pea. *(pea = die Erbse)* ....

   c) The old shirt. *(shirt = Hemd)* ....

   d) The trousers are big. *(trousers = die Hose)* ....

   e) A green pullover. *(pullover = der Pullover)* ....

   f) The jacket is blue. *(jacket = die Jacke)* ....

Making Comparisons

Q1 Match up the German words on the left with the English equivalent on the right.

Länger	Shorter
Größer	Cheaper
Älter	Older
Kürzer	Prettier
Billiger	Faster
Schöner	Bigger
Schneller	Longer

Q2 Our typist has mixed up all the letters in the following words. Write them out in the correct order. The bits in brackets tell you what the should mean.

a) ßgrteö *(biggest)* ....

b) tttsssreeineean *(most interesting)* ....

c) testeäl *(oldest)* ....

d) cheestnsll *(fastest)* ....

e) blliigets *(cheapest)* ....

Q3 Write out the following in German.

a) Dave is bigger than Geoff. ....

b) Smita is shorter than Julie. ....

c) James is smaller than Sandy. ....

d) Kathy is slower than Sarah. ....

e) Geoff is younger than Suresh. ....

f) Hans is older than Karl. ....

g) Lisa is nicer than Polly. ....

h) Thomas is faster than Dieter. ....

Words for 'You' — 'du', 'Sie' and 'ihr'

Q1 Write "du", "Sie" or "ihr" next to each person, to show which word you would use for "you" if you were speaking to them.

a) the Prime Minister ....

h) a teacher in school ....

b) a classmate ....

i) your best friend ....

c) your sister ....

j) your uncle ....

d) the Queen ....

e) a fireman ....

f) your parents ....

We will not be amused if you get it wrong.

g) your cat ....

Q2 Which of the following questions would you use with these people? Write out the correct version.

a) Your mum: *Wie heißt du?* **OR** *Wie heißen Sie?*

    ....

b) Policeman: *Wie alt bist du?* **OR** *Wie alt sind Sie?*

    ....

c) Adult stranger: *Sprechen Sie Deutsch?* **OR** *Sprichst du Deutsch?*

    ....

d) Your uncle: *Sind Sie verheiratet?* **OR** *Bist du verheiratet?*

    ....

e) Best friend: *Wie alt bist du?* **OR** *Wie alt sind Sie?*

    ....

Q3 Write down how you would say the following sentences in German:

a) How old are you? (talking to your dog) ....

b) Where do you live? (your uncle) ....

c) What's your name? (to the Prime Minister) ....

d) Where do you live? (the Queen) ....

e) Do you speak German? (person in the street) ....

Verbs — Present Tense

Q1 "fragen" follows the same pattern as "machen". For each of these, write the correct form of "fragen" from the box.

a) ich ....

b) du ....

c) er ....

f) wir ....

g) ihr ....

h) Sie ....

fragt   fragst

fragen   frage

fragt   fragen

Q2 Complete the sentences, by filling in the correct form of the verb in brackets. They all follow the same pattern as "machen".

a) Ich .... *(kaufen)*

b) Ihr .... Deutsch. *(verstehen)*

c) Sie (you, formal) .... Pizza. *(kaufen)*

d) Du .... *(fragen)*

e) Wir .... Fußball. *(spielen)*

f) Er .... einen Fehler. *(machen)*

Q3 Here are some scrap pieces of paper from Peter's notes in his German lesson. Fill in the missing bits. HINT: Watch out, these verbs don't follow the normal pattern.

a) Essen

ich ....

du isst

er ....

wir ....

ihr esst

Sie ....

b) Fahren

ich fahre

du ....

er fährt

wir ....

ihr ....

Sie fahren

c) Schlafen

ich schlafe

du...................

er ....

wir ....

ihr ....

Sie ....

Q4 Write the following in German. The verb you'll need is in brackets.

a) I go. *(fahren)* ....

b) They play football. *(spielen)* ....

c) She watches TV. *(fernsehen)* ....

d) They read books. *(lesen)* ....

e) We ask. *(fragen)* ....

Sein, Haben and Separable Verbs

Q1 Here are some of Peter's notes from his German lesson. Fill in the missing bits.

a) SEIN

ich bin

du ....

er/sie/es ....

wir ....

ihr ....

Sie ....

sie sind

b) HABEN

ich ....

du hast

er/sie/es ....

wir haben

ihr ....

Sie ....

sie haben

Q2 Unscramble the letters in these words. They're all separable verbs. I've done the first one for you.

a) ghnsauee *(to go out)* *ausgehen* ....

b) rfanneu *(to phone)* ....

c) kmmaoenn *(to arrive)* ....

d) afhebarn *(to leave)* ....

e) wschneaba *(to wash up)* ....

f) asshnuee *(to seem)* ....

Q3 The words in these sentences are in the wrong order. Write them out in the right order.

a) aus gehen wir ....

b) sechs steht ihr auf um Uhr ....

c) kommt Peter um an neun Uhr ....

d) du Sarah an rufst ....

e) Sie fahren ab drei Uhr um ....

f) ab Mutter wäscht meine ....

Q4 Write these in German. Remember that the verbs are made up of two bits.

a) They get up. ....

b) He goes out. ....

HINT: all the German verbs you need have already been used on this page.

c) She rings up. ....

d) We leave. ....

e) They arrive. ....

f) We wash up. ....

Modal Verbs

Q1 Draw lines to match up the following German verbs with their English meanings. I've done the first one for you.

wollen	to have to / must
mögen	to want
müssen	to like
dürfen	to be supposed to / should
sollen	to be allowed to
können	to be able to / can

Q2 The following German words have some spelling mistakes. Write them out correctly. I've done the first one for you.

a) *I want to* = ich wall *Ich will* ....

b) *you (formal) want to* = Sie wullen ....

c) *you (informal, singular) can* = du kunnst ....

d) *we can* = wir künnen ....

e) *he is allowed* = er durfst ....

Q3 Write these sentences out again, putting the words into the right order.

a) essen kann Peter
....

b) Sie Hunde mögen
....

c) soll schreiben ich
....

d) ich muss visitieren Spanien
....

Q4 Write the following out in German:

a) I want to sleep. ....

b) I like playing table tennis. ....

c) Am I allowed to go out? ....

d) I should wash up. ....

...And "model" verbs are just 3 inches high...
These modal verbs are dead useful — imagine trying to speak English without them. I bet you <u>can't</u>. Even if someone said you <u>should</u>. Even if you <u>want</u> to. See what I mean (he said smugly).

Commands and Orders

Q1 The words below are all telling someone what to do. Each of them is talking to a
different person: one person (friendly), two or more (friendly) or any number (polite).
Write the words from the left in the right boxes.

Lesen

Hör

Singt   Sprechen

Komm

Nehmen   Setzt

Lauf

Treten   Kommt

One person (friendly)	Two or more (friendly)	Any number (polite)

Q2 Here are some things people have been told not to do.
Write down what they mean in English.

a) Singt nicht!

....

b) Lauf nicht!

....

c) Kommt nicht!

....

d) Sprechen Sie nicht!

....

e) Lesen Sie nicht!

....

f) Hör nicht zu!

....

g) Sitzt nicht!

....

Q3 Write the following out in German. The bits in brackets tell you who you're talking to.

a) Sing! *(ihr)*

....

b) Don't speak! *(Sie)*

....

c) Be quiet! *(ihr)*

....

d) Sit! *(ihr)*

....

e) Go! *(du)*

....

f) Don't sing! *(Sie)*

....

g) Come! *(du)*

....

h) Don't go! *(ihr)*

....

Talking About the Past

Q1   The following sentences are in the past, but they have one word missing (the part of haben). Fill in the missing words.

   a) Er .... heute geschlafen.

   b) Sie .... es gebrochen.

   c) Wir .... gekocht.

   d) Ich............... einen Apfel gekauft.

   e) Du .... deine Mutter gesehen.

   f) Ich .... Tennis gespielt.

HINT: don't worry about what these mean, you only need to tackle the first bit.

Q2   Change each verb into the past tense form (the past participle), then write it out in English. I've done the first one for you.

   a) spielen *(to play)* ...... *gespielt (played)* ......

   b) fragen *(to ask)* ....

   c) hören *(to hear)* ....

   d) essen *(to eat)* ....

   e) trinken *(to drink)* ....

   f) schreiben *(to write)* ....

   g) sagen *(to say)* ....

   h) kaufen *(to buy)* ....

   i) machen *(to make / do)* ....

This darn hat is really getting on my wick.

Q3   Here is a note of what Mark has done this morning. Write it out in German, in full sentences. The verbs you need are all in Q2.

7.00	I played football.
8.30	I ate.
8.45	I bought milk.
9.30	I wrote to Dieter.
10.00	I drank apple juice.

....
....
....
....
....

*HINTS:
football = Fußball
milk = Milch
to Dieter = an Dieter
apple juice = Apfelsaft
music = Musik*

Talking About the Future

Q1   Rearrange these words to make proper sentences about the future.
The first one's been done for you.

a)   spüle Samstag am ich

Ich spüle am Samstag.
....

b)   fahre Jahr nach Spanien nächstes ich

....

c)   du hierhin nächste kommst Woche

....

d)   machst Montag am du das

....

Q2   Here's the future form of the verb "gehen". Fill in the missing vowels.

.....ch w.....rd..... gehen   w.....r w.....rd.....n gehen

d..... w.....rst gehen   .....hr w.....rd.....t gehen

.....r / s..... / .....s w.....rd gehen   S..... w.....rd.....n gehen

                                             s..... w.....rd.....n gehen

Q3   Write these sentences out **in German**.

a)   I will sing on Saturday.

....

b)   He will visit you tomorrow.

....

c)   She will go to Spain next week.

....

d)   Next year I will go to Portugal.

....

e)   I will clean tomorrow.

....

f)   They will sleep tomorrow.

....

Negatives — Nicht and Kein

Q1   Some of the following sentences are in the negative form, and some are positive. Write them out in the right place in the table below. I've done the first two for you.

Ich mag Käse nicht.

Das Haus ist gelb.

Ich bin nicht sportlich.

Sie ist Sabine.

Sie ist meine Mutter.

Ich spiele nicht gern Fußball.

Negative Form	Positive Form
Ich mag Käse nicht.	Das Haus ist gelb.

Q2   Draw lines to match up the German sentences and their English meanings.

Gary ist nicht hier.

Ich habe keinen Hund.

Mein Haus hat keinen Garten.

Sie singt nicht.

She doesn't sing.

My house doesn't have a garden.

Gary is not here.

I don't have a dog.

Q3   Write the following sentences in the negative form. Then say what they mean in English. I've done the first one for you.

a)   Wir haben Bananen. *(We have bananas.)*

    Wir haben keine Bananen. (We have no bananas.)

b)   Die Lampe ist rot. *(The lamp is red.)*

....

c)   Ich habe einen Bruder. *(I have a brother.)*

....

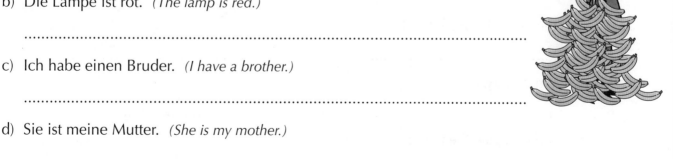

d)   Sie ist meine Mutter. *(She is my mother.)*

....

e)   Bettina isst einen Apfel. *(Bettina eats an apple.)*

....

f)   Ich bin Spanier. *(I am Spanish.)*

....

Section 8 — Grammar and Phrases

Word Order 1

Q1   Rearrange these words to make proper sentences. Think about the word order. Think hard.

a) Hunger ich habe   ....

b) Fußball ich heute spiele   ....

c) du kein heute hast Essen   ....

d) Kino ich ins gehe   ....

e) ich Tee trinke   ....

f) Berlinerin sie ist   ....

Q2   Use one of the words on the right to link the two bits of each sentence.

a) Ich habe heute Hunger .... ich habe nichts zum Essen. *AND*

b) Ich spiele Fußball .... Klavier. *AND*

c) Du fährst mit dem Bus .... ich gehe ins Kino. *BUT*

d) Ich esse Pizza .... Currywurst. *OR*

e) Sie sprechen Deutsch .... sie wohnen hier. *BUT*

f) Wir machen unsere Hausaufgaben .... wir sehen fern. *OR*

und

aber

oder

Q3   Write these sentences out **in German**. Remember to put the time bit first.

a) Today they are playing football.

    ....

b) Today I'm hungry.

    ....

c) On Mondays I play the piano.

    ....

d) Today you have nothing to eat.

    ....

e) On Saturdays she reads.

    ....

Word Order 2

Q1   Draw lines to match the German words to their English meanings.

weil   wenn   obwohl

although   because   if

Q2   Join these phrases together, and write them out as **one sentence**, using the German for the joining word shown. I've done the first one for you. HINT: Watch out for the word order.

a)   Ich spiele Fußball. + **IF** + Ich habe Zeit.
(I play football. + IF + I have time.)
Ich spiele Fußball, wenn ich Zeit habe.

b)   Ich koche nicht gern. + **ALTHOUGH** + Essen ist toll.
(I hate cooking. + ALTHOUGH + Food is terrific.)
....

c)   Ich habe Hunger. + **BECAUSE** + Ich habe heute morgen Fußball gespielt.
(I am hungry. + BECAUSE + I played football this morning.)
....

d)   Meine Mutter spielt Fußball. + **ALTHOUGH** + Es ist neblig.
(My mother is playing football. + ALTHOUGH + It's foggy.)
....

Q3   Here are some more phrases to join together as one sentence.
This time the "weil", "wenn" or "obwohl" should go at the **beginning** of the sentence you write. Remember any changes you need to make to the word order.

a)   **IF** + Es ist kalt. + Ich komme mit dem Bus.
(IF + It's cold. + I come by bus.)
Wenn es kalt ist, komme ich mit dem Bus.

b)   **ALTHOUGH** + Ich mag Kaffee. + Ich hasse Tee.
(ALTHOUGH + I like coffee. + I hate Tea.)
....

c)   **IF** + Ich stehe um fünf Uhr auf. + Ich trinke Kaffee.
(IF + I get up at five o'clock. + I drink coffee.)
....

d)   **BECAUSE** + Sie gehen ins Kino. + Sie rufen ein Taxi an.
(BECAUSE + They are going to the cinema. + They call a taxi.)
....

Third oldest joke in the world...

Order word German in difficult can be. (Nurse, my sides.) Don't worry if you find this page tough going — it <u>is</u>. At least make sure you get the stuff on <u>p.64</u> fixed in your head — it's <u>essential</u>.

Section 8 — Grammar and Phrases

Boring But Important Tables

Q1 Fill in the missing bits of these verbs.

PRESENT tense — spielen, to play
ich spiele
du ....
er / sie / es ....
wir ....
ihr ....
Sie spielen
sie ....

PAST tense — kaufen, to buy
ich ....
du hast gekauft
er / sie / es ....
wir ....
ihr habt gekauft
Sie ....
sie ....

FUTURE tense — schwimmen, to swim
ich ....
du ....
er / sie / es wird schwimmen
wir werden schwimmen
ihr ....
Sie ....
sie ....

PRESENT tense — sein, to be
ich ....
du bist
er / sie / es ....
wir ....
ihr seid
Sie ....
sie ....

Q2 The fun's almost over. Fill in the missing bits of these words.

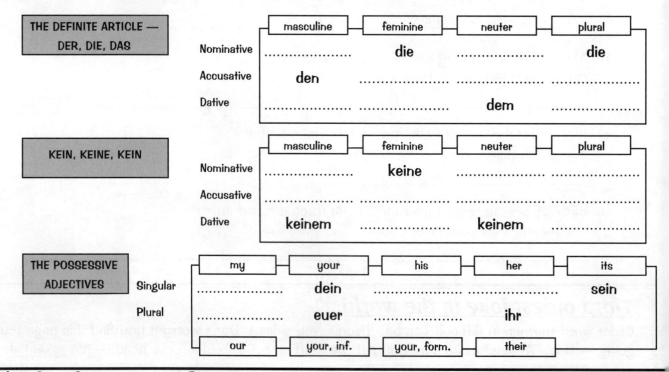

THE DEFINITE ARTICLE — DER, DIE, DAS

	masculine	feminine	neuter	plural
Nominative	....	die	....	die
Accusative	den	....	....	....
Dative	....	....	dem	....

KEIN, KEINE, KEIN

	masculine	feminine	neuter	plural
Nominative	....	keine	....	....
Accusative	....	....	....	....
Dative	keinem	....	keinem	....

THE POSSESSIVE ADJECTIVES

	my	your	his	her	its
Singular	....	dein	....	....	sein
Plural	....	euer	....	ihr	
	our	your, inf.	your, form.	their	

Giant Crossword

Q1   Use the clues to complete this crossword. All the answers should be **in German**.

ACROSS
2) German for "thank you" (5)
5) German for "knee" (4)
7) I'm called Bob
   = ... heiße Bob (3)
9) German for "yes" (2)
11) This verb means "to go" (6)
12) The polite way to say "you"
    (3)
13) What are you called?
    = Wie .... du? (5)
14) The opposite of "day" (5)
18) You have one every year.
    You get cards, and a cake. (10)

20) "doctor" (4)
21) Small, round, green
    vegetables, usually
    mushy or frozen (6)
24) The colour you get
    when you mix "rot"
    and "gelb" (6)
26) What you sit on (5)
27) Small red fruit, often
    eaten with cream (8)
28) German for "garden" (6)
DOWN
1) fünf + zwei =.... (5)
3) "goodbye" (3, 11)

4) Where milk comes from (3)
6) This verb means "to eat" (5)
8) German for "shirt" (4)
10) sechs + zwei =.... (4)
12) "town" (5)
15) The day after yesterday (5)
16) You have one on each side
    of your head (3)
17) Day after "Donnerstag" (7)
19) Opposite of bad (3)
22) "North" (4)
23) What you smell with (4)
25) I like swimming = Ich
    schwimme .... (4)

Giant Picture Quiz

Q1   For KS3 German, you should know the German for all these things. In each box, write the German for the thing the arrow points to. Don't forget the "der", "die" or "das" to go in front.

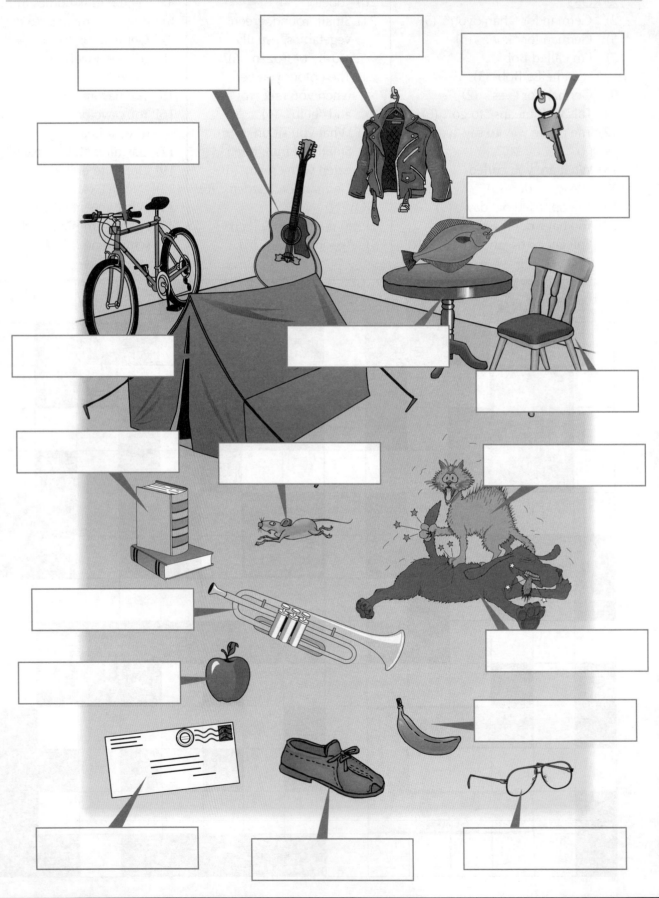

Answers

Page 1

Q1　f) 86
　b) 92　g) 3
　c) 12　h) 10
　d) 31　i) 5
　e) 25　j) 16

Q2　b) dreiundzwanzig
　c) neunundachtzig
　d) vierzehn
　e) siebenunddreißig
　f) einundneunzig
　g) achtundfünfzig
　h) siebzehn
　i) einundvierzig
　j) zweiundsiebzig
　k) eins
　l) hundert

Q3　e) 9th
　b) 8th　f) 3rd
　c) 7th　g) 14th
　d) 5th　h) 12th

Q4　b) elfte
　c) zweite
　d) sechste
　e) vierte
　f) erste

Page 2

Q1　b) Es ist zehn vor vier.
　c) Es ist fünf nach sieben.
　d) Es ist Viertel vor drei.
　e) Es ist zwanzig nach eins.
　f) Es ist halb neun.
　g) Es ist fünf vor sechs.
　h) Es ist fünfundzwanzig vor zwölf.

Q2　b) zweiundzwanzig Uhr fünfundzwanzig
　c) elf Uhr fünfundfünfzig
　d) dreizehn Uhr

Q3　a) tomorrow　g) today
　b) week　h) weekend
　c) evening　i) morning
　d) month　j) night
　e) afternoon　k) yesterday
　f) day　l) year

Page 3

Q1　a) May　g) March
　b) January　h) August
　c) October　i) June
　d) April　j) September
　e) July　k) November
　f) February　l) December

Q2

Page 3 (cont.)

Q3　b) am sechzehnten April
　c) am ersten Juli
　d) am achtundzwanzigsten Februar
　e) am dritten September
　f) am neunundzwanzigsten Mai

Q4　a) am fünfundzwanzigsten Dezember
　b) am ersten Januar
　c) am fünften November

Page 4

Q1

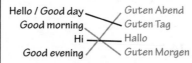

Q2　b) auf Wiedersehen
　c) bis später
　d) gute Nacht

Q3　b) guten Abend
　c) gute Nacht
　d) guten Morgen
　e) hallo
　f) guten Tag
　g) auf Wiedersehen
　h) tschüss

Page 5

Q1　a) danke　d) geht
　b) dir　e) schön
　c) geht's

Q2　a) Darf ich Ihnen Bernd vorstellen?
　b) Darf ich Ihnen meine Freundin vorstellen?
　c) Darf ich euch Bernd vorstellen?
　d) Darf ich dir Bernd vorstellen?

Q3　b) Schön, dich kennen zu lernen.
　c) Schön, Sie kennen zu lernen.
　d) Wie geht es Ihnen?
　e) Gut, danke.

Page 6

Q1

Q2　a) Leid　d) schön
　b) schön　e) ja
　c) danke　f) entschuldigen

Q3　a) Nein, danke.
　b) Entschuldigen Sie, wo ist das Museum bitte?
　c) Bitte (schön).
　d) Es tut mir Leid, aber ich mag Äpfel nicht.
　e) Bitte schön.
　f) Entschuldigen Sie, wo ist das Kino bitte?
　g) Ja, bitte.
　h) Es tut mir Leid, aber ich mag Karotten nicht.

Page 7

Q1　a) I want
　b) please
　c) I would like
　d) May I

Q2　a) Darf ich Ihnen helfen den Tisch zu decken?
　b) Es tut mir Leid, aber ich esse Fleisch nicht.
　c) Darf ich Ihnen helfen das Essen zubereiten?
　d) Darf ich Ihnen spülen helfen?

Q3　b) Ich möchte hier sitzen.
　c) Ich möchte ein Brötchen.
　d) Ich möchte spülen.

Page 8

Q1

Q2　a) Ich bin klein
　b) Ich trage eine Brille.
　c) Ich habe blaue Augen.
　d) Ich bin groß.
　e) Ich habe schwarze Haare.
　f) Ich bin nett und fleißig.

Q3　a) F　b) F　c) T
　d) T　e) F　f) T

Page 9

Q1　a) my sister
　b) my grandmother
　c) my cousin (female)
　d) my friend
　e) my uncle
　f) my stepmother
　g) my stepbrother

Q2　a) 10
　b) Petra's father.
　c) Petra's aunt.
　d) Bob
　e) Petra's cousin (male)
　f) Her cousin, Rob.

Q3　meine Großmutter: Katy;
　mein Großvater: David;
　meine Tante: Amy;
　mein Onkel: Thomas;
　mein Cousin: Paul;
　meine Cousine: Hayley.

Page 10

Q1　a) das Pferd　c) der Hund
　b) die Maus　d) die Katze

Q2　a) der Vogel
　b) der Hund
　c) das Kaninchen

Answers

d) die Kuh
e) der Hamster
f) die Schildkröte

Q3 b) Ich habe ein Kaninchen.
c) Sie hat einen Hamster.
d) Du hast eine Katze.
e) Mein Hund ist böse.
f) Meine Schildkröte heißt "Speedy".

Q4 a) Ich habe ein Hund.
b) Sie hat einen Hamster.
c) Ich habe keine Haustiere.
d) Mein Vogel ist groß.
e) Meine Katze heißt "Fluffy".
f) Du hast einen Hund.

Page 11
Q1

kitchen — die Küche
dining room — das Esszimmer
living room — das Wohnzimmer
bedroom — das Schlafzimmer
garden — der Garten
bathroom — das Badezimmer

Q2 a) ein
b) Haus
c) Zu .... Küche
d) Was
e) gibt
f) es

Q3 a) Yes   d) 6
b) Three   e) 4
c) No, only 1

Q4 Many acceptable answers.

Page 12
Q1 a) I live in a city.
b) I live in a house.
c) I live in the countryside.
d) I live at the seaside.
e) I live in a village.

Q2 a) Ich wohne in den Bergen.
b) Ich wohne in London.
c) Ich wohne in Leeds, einer Großstadt in Nordengland.
d) Ich lebe gern hier, weil es fantastich ist.
e) Ich lebe nicht gern hier, weil es zu ruhig ist.

Q3 a) T   b) F   c) F
d) F   e) F   f) F
g) T   h) T

Page 13
Q1 Ich wache auf.
Ich stehe auf.
Ich ziehe mich an.
Ich esse Frühstück.
Ich gehe in die Schule.
Ich gehe nach Hause.
Ich sehe fern.
Ich gehe ins Bett.

Q2 a) Ich wasche mich.

b) Ich esse Abendessen.
c) Ich mache meine Hausaufgaben.
d) Ich ziehe mich an.
e) Ich gehe ins Bett.
f) Ich gehe in die Schule.
g) Ich wache auf.
h) Ich esse Frühstück.

Q3 a) At seven o'clock.
b) He goes to school.
c) Have breakfast.
d) At six o'clock.
e) He goes home.
f) He has a wash.
g) At nine o'clock.

Page 14
Q1

I wash the car — Ich wasche das Auto
I make my bed — Ich mache mein Bett
I do the cleaning — Ich putze
I wash the dishes — Ich spüle
Ich mache nichts — I don't do anything
Ich sauge Staub — I do the vacuum cleaning
Ich räume mein Zimmer auf — I tidy my room
Ich gehe einkaufen — I do the shopping

Q2 b) Ich decke den Tisch.
c) Ich mache mein Bett.
d) Ich putze.
e) Ich spüle.
f) Ich räume mein Zimmer auf.

Q3 a) wasche   d) putze
b) nichts   e) sauge
c) mache   f) decke

Q4 a) Ich spüle.
b) Ich putze.
c) Ich mache nichts.
d) Ich decke den Tisch.

Page 15
Q1 a) der Hals   e) der Kopf
b) der Arm   f) der Bauch
c) die Hand   g) der Finger
d) das Bein   h) der Fuß

Q2 a) das Knie   d) der Finger
b) das Bein   e) der Bauch
c) der Rücken   f) der Hals

Q3 a) das Auge   d) die Nase
b) das Ohr   e) der Zahn (or die Zähne)
c) die Haare   f) der Mund

Page 16
Q1

chemist's — die Apotheke
hospital — das Krakenhaus
I want to go to the doctors — Ich will zum Arzt gehen
doctor — der Arzt
I am ill — Ich bin krank

Q2 a) Mein Rücken tut mir weh
b) Mein Finger tut mir weh
c) Ich habe Kopfschmerzen
d) Mein Hals tut mir weh
e) Ich habe Bauchschmerzen

Q3 a) Prescription   d) Cream
b) Plaster   e) Medicine

c) Tablet   f) Painkiller

Q4 a) Ich habe Bauchschmerzen
b) Meine Nase tut mir weh
c) Ich habe Ohrenschmerzen
d) Mein Bein tut mir weh
e) Mein Rücken tut mir weh
f) Ich habe Kopfschmerzen

Page 17
Q1
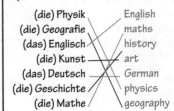

(die) Physik — physics
(die) Geografie — geography
(das) Englisch — English
(die) Kunst — art
(das) Deutsch — German
(die) Geschichte — history
(die) Mathe — maths

Q2 a) (die) Informatik
b) (die) Chemie
c) (die) Naturwissenschaft
d) (die) Musik
e) (die) Biologie
f) (die) Reli(gion)
g) (der) Sport
h) (das) Französisch
i) (das) Spanisch

Q3 a) German
b) No
c) Yes
d) Music
e) English
f) Because it's boring.
g) Because it's interesting.

Page 18
Q1 i) B   v) G
ii) C   vi) E
iii) A   vii) D
iv) F

Q2 a) Fahrrad
b) Stunden
c) fängt
d) Fuß
e) Minuten
f) stehe

Q3 7.00 Ich stehe um sieben Uhr auf.
7.30 Ich esse Frühstück um sieben Uhr dreißig.
8.30 Die Schule fängt um acht Uhr dreißig an.
3.00 Die Schule ist um drei Uhr aus.
We have 7 lessons per day... Wir haben sieben Stunden pro Tag.

Q4 Many acceptable answers.

Page 19
Q1 a) Stand up!
b) Be quiet!
c) How do you say that in German?
d) What does that mean?
e) Listen!
f) Sit down!

Answers

Q2 a) timetable   d)   ruler
    b) pen   e)   exercise book
    c) rubber   f)   book
                    g)   teacher (male)

Q3 a) Wie sagt man das auf Deutsch?
    b) Steht auf!
    c) richtig
    d) Was bedeutet das?
    e) Hört zu!
    f) die Lehrerin
    g) der Schüler
    h) der Bleistift
    i) die Uniform
    j) der Stundenplan
    k) im Klassenzimmer

Page 20

Q1 a) mechanic
    b) salesperson
    c) actor
    d) hairdresser
    e) engineer
    f) builder
    g) dentist
    h) policeman
    i) secretary
    j) doctor

Q2 a) hairdresser
    b) actress
    c) office worker
    d) builder
    e) salesperson
    f) nurse
    g) doctor
    h) policewoman
    i) engineer
    j) teacher

Q3

Male	Female
Friseur	Bauarbeiterin
Büroangestellter	Krankenschwester
Schauspieler	Mechanikerin
Krankenpfleger	Polizistin
Arzt	Ingenieurin
Zahnarzt	Lehrerin

Q4 a) Friseur
    b) Bauarbeiterin
    c) Sekretärin
    d) Zahnarzt
    e) Polizistin
    f) Sekretär
    g) Ingenieurin
    h) Schauspieler
    i) Lehrerin

Page 21

Q1

Ich bin Arzt — I am a doctor
Mein Vater ist Mechaniker — My father is a mechanic
Meine Mutter ist Verkäuferin — My mother is a salesperson
Mein Freund George ist Ingenieur — My friend George is an engineer
Ich arbeite bei Kwik Save — I work in Kwik Save
Ich habe einen Teilzeitjob. — I have a part-time job

Q2 a) I want to study sports.
    b) I want to be a dentist.
    c) I want to study German because it is easy.

d) I want to study maths because I want to be a teacher.
e) I want to be an actor because they earn a lot of money.

Q3 a) es einfach ist
    b) sie viel Geld verdienen
    c) ich Lehrer werden möchte
    d) es lustig ist

Page 22

Q1 a) take the second street on the left
    b) take the third street on the right
    c) go right
    d) go left
    e) go straight on

Q2 a) Gehen Sie geradeaus. Nehmen Sie die zweite Straße rechts. Gehen Sie links. / Nehmen Sie die erste Straße links.
    b) (Ja.) Gehen Sie geradeaus. Nehmen Sie die vierte Straße links. Gehen Sie rechts.
    c) (Ja.) Gehen Sie geradeaus. Nehmen Sie die dritte Straße rechts.
    d) Gehen Sie rechts. Nehmen Sie die erste Straße links. Nehmen Sie die erste Straße rechts. / Gehen Sie rechts.
    e) (Ja.) Gehen Sie links. Gehen Sie rechts. Nehmen Sie die erste Straße links. / Gehen Sie links.

Q3 a) Sie ist drei Kilometer von hier.
    b) Es ist fünf / sechs Kilometer von hier.
    c) Es ist ein / fünf Kilometer von hier.

Page 23

Q1 b) das Süßwarengeschäft
    c) die Buchhandlung
    d) die Konditorei
    e) die Metzgerei
    f) der Lebensmittelladen
    g) die Apotheke
    h) die Bäckerei

Q2 a) He's looking for the chemist's.
    b) It's a kilometre away.
    c) He should take the third street on the right.
    d) She wants to go to the bookshop.
    e) It's 2 kilometres away.
    f) She should turn left first of all.

Page 24

Q1

das Kino — cinema
das Verkehrsbüro — tourist office
die Bibliothek — library
das Schloss — castle
der Bahnhof — train station
das Krankenhaus — hospital
die Stadtmitte — town centre
das Schwimmbad — swimming pool

Q2 a) She wants to go to the church first.
    b) She must go straight on and then take the second street on the left.

c) The castle is 5 kilometres away.
d) No, there isn't a bookshop near the tourist office.
e) The library is a kilometre away.

Q3 a) Wo ist das Rathaus, bitte?
    b) Und wo ist das Postamt, bitte?
    c) Wie weit ist es von hier?
    d) Gibt es hier in der Nähe ein Freizeitzentrum?
    e) Danke.

Page 25

Q1 a) das Lammfleisch
    b) die Meeresfrüchte
    c) das Schweinefleisch
    d) das Rindfleisch
    e) der Schinken
    f) das Hähnchen

Q2

Supermarket:	Grocer's:
a sausage,	two lemons,
fish,	a pear,
steak,	an apple,
mushrooms,	an onion,
a cauliflower,	peas,
four potatoes,	three peaches,
a cabbage,	a banana,
a lettuce,	four oranges
five carrots	

Q3 MARGHERITA: Tomatoes
PROSCIUTTO: Tomatoes, Ham, Mushrooms
AI FUNGHI: Tomatoes, Mushrooms, Onions
TOMATENSALAT: Tomatoes, Carrots, Lettuce, Onions
OBSTSALAT: Apples, Strawberries, Oranges

Q4 Prosciutto

Page 26

Q1 a) i)   Kaffee
       ii)   Mineralwasser
       iii)   Orangensaft
       iv)   heiße Schokolade
       v)   Cola

    b) Apfelsaft   apple juice
       Bier   beer
       Rotwein   red wine
       Weißwein   white wine
       Tee   tea

Q2 a) der Keks
    b) die Kartoffelchips
    c) der Käse
    d) das Ei
    e) die Pommes frites
    f) das Eis
    g) das Brot
    h) die Marmelade

Q3 b) "Kartoffelchips", because crisps aren't sweet.
    c) "Getreideflocken", because cereal isn't a dairy product.
    d) "Milch", because milk isn't alcoholic.

Answers

e) "Cola", because coke isn't a hot drink.
f) "Heiße Schokolade", because hot chocolate isn't a cold drink.
g) "Suppe", because soup is runny.

Page 27
Q1 a) Hast du Durst? / Haben Sie Durst?
b) Ich mag Schokolade nicht.
c) Ich habe Hunger.
d) Ich mag Marmelade nicht.
e) Ich habe keinen Durst.
f) Ich mag Milch.

Q2 a) At 7 o'clock.
b) Cereal and coffee.
c) She eats pork and rice, and drinks coke.
d) At 1 o'clock.
e) She eats chicken and pasta, and drinks white wine.

Q3 a) Es ist um sechs Uhr.
b) Ich esse Brot. Ich trinke Tee.
c) Ich trinke Mineralwasser.

Page 28
Q1

das Dessert ———— waiter
die Kellnerin ———— waitress
das Getränk ———— drink
der Kellner ———— menu
die Vorspeise ———— starter
die Speisekarte ———— main course
das Hauptgericht ———— dessert

Q2 a) Einen Tisch für eine Person, bitte.
b) Ich hätte gern ein Bier.
c) Ich hätte gern die Suppe.
d) Haben Sie Lammfleisch?
e) Ich hätte gern Lammfleisch, Kartoffeln und Erbsen.

Q3 a) Ich möchte einen Tisch reservieren.
b) Ich hätte gern Kohl.

Q4 a) Zahlen, bitte.
b) Service charge included.

Page 29
Q1 b) die Schuhe
c) der Rock
d) das T-Shirt
e) das Kleid
f) die Socken
g) die Hose
h) der Pullover

Q2 b) Mrs Becker wears a pink raincoat.
c) Tobias wears green trousers.
d) Anna wears a white skirt.
e) My father wears a grey hat.
f) Sophie wears an orange T-shirt.
g) She wears a yellow blouse.
h) He wears a red tie.

Q3 a) Sie trägt eine gelbe Bluse, einen blauen Rock, und schwarze Schuhe.
b) Er trägt einen grüne Pullover, und eine braune Hose.

Page 30
Q1 a) Anything else?
b) I'll leave it.
c) It's 10 euros.
d) I'll take that one.
e) I'd like a pair of trousers.
f) How much is that?
g) Do you have a raincoat?

Q2 a) Haben Sie ein gelbes T-Shirt?
b) Ich lasse es.
c) Ja, bitte. Haben Sie einen gelben Hut?
d) Ich nehme das. Danke.
e) Haben Sie einen Wollpullover?
f) Nein, danke. Ich möchte einen blauen Pullover.
g) Ja. Ich nehme das.
h) Nein, danke. Was kostet das?

Page 31
Q1 a) Fußball
b) Federball
c) Rugby
d) Tischtennis
e) Schach
f) Tennis
g) Kricket

Q2 a) die Gitarre
b) die Trompete
c) das Klavier
d) die Klarinette
e) das Cello
f) die Geige
g) das Schlagzeug

Q3 NB: You could put the instruments/sports in a different order.
a) Ich spiele Kricket, Trompete und Schach.
b) Ich spiele Klavier, Geige und Federball.
c) Ich spiele Fußball und Tennis und ich spiele Schlagzeug.
d) Ich spiele Klarinette, Schach und Tischtennis.
e) Ich spiele Cello, Geige und Kricket.

Page 32
Q1 a) fahre   d) gehe
b) gehe   e) gehe
c) schwimme

Q2 b) Ich gehe wandern.
c) Ich gehe einkaufen.
d) Ich gehe Schlittschuh laufen.
e) Ich fahre Rad

Q3 b) Ich liebe Federball.
c) Ich mag Schach nicht.
d) Ich hasse Tennis.
e) Ich mag Kricket.

Q4 b) , weil es einfach ist.
c) , weil es langweilig ist.
d) , weil es ermüdend ist.
e) , weil es interessant ist.

Page 33
Q1 a) I listen to music.
b) I read magazines.
c) I watch films.
d) I read novels.

Q2 a) Ich lese gern Romane.
b) Ich höre nicht gern Radio.
c) Ich sehe gern fern.
d) Ich lese night gern Zeitungen.
e) Ich lese gern Bücher.

Q3 b) Ich mag diesen Film.
c) Ich mag dieses Zeitschrift.
d) Ich mag diese Zeitung.

Q4 a) magazines and newspapers
b) violin
c) she likes shopping

Page 34
Q1 b) das Freizeitzentrum
c) das Kino
d) das Schwimmbad
e) das Restaurant
f) das Theater
g) nach Hause

Q2 a) Ja, gerne.
b) Nein, danke.
c) Ich habe kein Geld.
d) Ja, das wäre schön.
e) Ich mache meine Hausaufgaben.
f) Ich gehe nicht gern ins Restaurant.

Q3 a) Hast du Lust ins Schwimmbad zu gehen?
b) Hast du Lust ins Kino zu gehen?
c) Hast du Lust in die Stadtmitte zu gehen?

Page 35
Q1

Treffen wir uns morgen. — Let's meet at 9 o'clock (am).
Treffen wir uns um neun Uhr. — Let's meet at 9 o'clock (pm).
Treffen wir uns heute Abend. — Let's meet on Saturday.
Treffen wir uns um einundzwanzig Uhr. — Let's meet this evening.
Treffen wir uns morgen früh. — Let's meet tomorrow.
Treffen wir uns am Sonnabend — Let's meet tomorrow morning.

Q2 a) Treffen wir uns vor dem Museum.
b) Treffen wir uns im Restaurant.
c) Treffen wir uns bei mir zu Hause.
d) Treffen wir uns im Park.
e) Treffen wir uns vor der Bank.

Q3 You: Hast du Lust ins Kino zu gehen?
You: Treffen wir uns um neunzehn Uhr.
You: Treffen wir uns vor dem Verkehrsamt.

Q4 You: Was kostet eine Karte, bitte?
You: Ich möchte vier Karten, bitte.
You: Danke (schön).

Page 36
Q1 a) das Auto   c) das Motorrad
b) das Fahrrad   d) das Flugzeug

Q2 a) coach   d) tram
b) underground   e) train
c) ship   f) bus

Answers

Q3 b) Ich fahre mit dem Auto.
   c) Ich fahre mit dem Motorrad.
   d) Ich reise mit dem Flugzeug. / Ich fliege.
   e) Ich fahre mit dem Fahrrad.
   f) Ich gehe zu Fuß.

Page 37

Q1

	Where	How
a)	Mainz	car
b)	Bonn	foot
c)	school	bicycle
d)	Italy	coach
e)	France	plane

Q2 b) drei einfache Fahrkarten zweite Klasse
   c) eine Rückfahrkart zweite Klasse
   d) vier einfache Fahrkarten erste Klasse
   e) zwei Rückfahrkarten zweite Klasse

Q3 a) When does the train for Mannheim leave?
   b) Which platform does the train leave from?
   c) Is there a train to Hamburg?

Q4 a) Der Zug nach Mannheim fährt um achtzehn Uhr ab.
   b) Der Zug fährt von Gleis zwölf ab.
   c) Ja, ein Zug fährt nach Hamburg.

Page 38

Q1 b) ein Brief
   c) ein Briefkasten
   d) eine Briefmarke
   e) eine Postkarte

Q2 a) It'll cost her 1 euro and 12 cents.
   b) She's sending her letter to Austria.
   c) She also wants a one-euro stamp.
   d) He's sending a postcard to France.
   e) It'll cost 51 cents.
   f) He also wants a three-euro stamp.

Q3 a) Hallo. Hier spricht .... Kann ich bitte mit Katharina sprechen?
   b) Wo ist sie, bitte?
   c) Meine Telefonnummer ist sechsundsiebzig, siebenunddreißig, fünfzehn. Danke, Frau Schulz.

Page 39

Q1 a) Thanks for your letter.
   b) Best wishes
   c) Write soon.
   d) See you soon.
   e) How are you?

Q2 a) Sam is a girl. (Lukas used "Liebe Sam", not "Lieber Sam".)
   b) I was very pleased to hear from you again.
   c) He says it's boring and difficult.
   d) Write soon.

Q3 *Many acceptable answers, but the following should be included.*
   Manchester, den 1. Juni
   Lieber Lukas,
   vielen Dank für deinen Brief.

Wie geht's?
Mein Lieblingsfach ist Geschichte, weil sie interessant ist.
Viele Grüße,
Sam

Page 40

Q1 a) Mit freundlichen Grüßen
   b) Vielen Dank im Voraus
   c) Sehr geehrte Damen und Herren
   d) Sehr geehrter Herr Werner

Q2 a) Sehr geehrter Herr Fischer
   b) Sehr geehrte Damen und Herren
   c) Many thanks in advance.

Q3 (your name and address)
   Großbritannien
   (your hometown), den (today's date in numbers separated by full stops)
   Sehr geehrter Herr Neumann, wenn möglich möchte ich bei Ihnen ein Doppelzimmer reservieren, vom 23. bis zum 28. Oktober. Könnten Sie mich bitte informieren, wie viel es kosten wird?
   Vielen Dank im Voraus.
   Mit freundlichen Grüßen,
   (your name)

Page 41

Q1 a) es ist heiß
   b) es ist sonnig
   c) es ist kalt
   d) es ist windig

Q2 b) Es ist bewölkt
   c) Es ist regnet
   d) Es ist sonnig
   e) Es ist kalt
   f) Es ist windig
   g) Es ist gut
   h) Es schneit

Q3 der Sommer = Summer
   der Winter = Winter
   der Frühling = Spring
   der Herbst = Autumn

Q4 a) Es schneit
   b) Wie ist das Wetter?
   c) Es ist schlecht
   d) Es ist stürmisch

Page 42

Q1
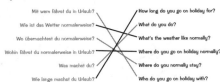

Q2 a) Spain
   b) rainy
   c) goes to the beach/swims
   d) 10 days
   e) in a hotel

Q3 a) Normalerweise fahre ich nach Frankreich.
   b) Ich fahre mit meiner Tante.
   c) Ich übernachte in einer Jugendherberge.

Page 43

Q1 a) campsite
   b) youth hostel
   c) pitch (space for a tent)
   d) caravan
   e) sleeping bag
   f) drinking water

Q2 a) der Speisesaal
   b) die Toilette
   c) das Telefon
   d) ein Zimmer
   e) Dusche
   f) Balkon
   g) Bad

Q3 b) Ein Doppelzimmer mit Balkon.
   c) Ein Einzelzimmer mit Toilette.
   d) Ein Einzelzimmer mit Dusche
   e) Ein Doppelzimmer mit Bad.

Page 44

Q1
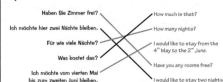

Q2 a) Haben Sie Zimmer frei?
   b) Ich möchte ein Doppelzimmer
   c) Ich möchte hier zwei Wochen bleiben. Was kostet das?

Q3 a) F   b) F   c) F
   d) T   e) T

Page 45

Q1 b) Holland
   c) Deutschland
   d) Spanien
   e) Italien
   f) Wales
   g) England
   h) Österreich
   i) Schottland
   j) Nordirland
   k) Irland
   l) die Schweiz
   m) Portugal
   n) Belgien

Q2   f) Österreich
   b) Belgien   g) die Schweiz
   c) Portugal   h) Irland
   d) Spanien   i) Italien
   e) Deutschland

Q3 a) Deutschland
   b) Schottland
   c) Nordirland
   d) Großbritannien
   e) das Vereinigte Königreich
   f) Frankreich

Answers

Page 46

Q1 a) Scotland
b) Northern Ireland
c) Wales
d) England

Q2 b) Ich bin Nordirländer
c) Ich bin Irin
d) Ich bin Schottin
e) Ich bin Waliser
f) Ich bin Engländerin

Q3 a) Germany e) Pablo
b) Italian f) Scotland
c) Lucy g) England
d) France

Page 47

Q1 a) Ich mag Tee.
b) Ich liebe Mathe.
c) Ich mag Kaffee nicht.
d) Ich hasse Goldfische.
e) Ich mag Deutsch.
f) Ich mag Naturwissenschaften nicht.

Q2 a) schwimme
b) Ich
c) gern

Q3 b) toll
c) doof
d) fantastisch
e) einfach Klasse
f) anstrengend
g) schwer
h) interessant

Q4 a) Geschichte ist toll.
b) Geschichte ist anstrengend.
c) Geschichte ist schwer.
d) Geschichte ist gut.
e) Geschichte ist fantastisch.

Page 48

Q1

Q2 b) Wohin e) Warum
c) Wann f) Wie
d) Wo g) Was

Q3 b) Heißt er Romeo?
(Is he called Romeo?)
c) Hast du einen Hund?
(Do you have a dog?)
d) Lernen wir Deutsch?
(Are we studying German?)
e) Gibt es hier in der Nähe ein Schloss?
(Is there a castle near here?)

Page 49

Q1 Katze, Fußball, Freund, Schuh, Zeit

Q2 DER: Schuh, Kuli, Hund,
    Onkel, Bruder, Vater
DIE: Tante, Cousine, Katze,
    Schwester, Freundin
DAS: Pferd, Haus, Ohr, Knie

Q3

Katze ———— Sofas
Hund ———— Hunde
Schuh ———— Bananen
Banane ———— Betten
Tante ———— Katzen
Freund ———— Schuhe
Sofa ———— Freunde
Bett ———— Tanten

Page 50

Q1 b) ein Hund
c) ein Schuh
d) eine Banane
e) eine Tante
f) ein Cousin
g) ein Freund
h) ein Sofa
i) ein Bett

Q2 b) mein Schuh
c) mein Kuli
d) mein Hund
e) meine Katze
f) mein Onkel
g) meine Schwester
h) mein Bruder
i) mein Vater
j) meine Freundin
k) meine Tante
l) mein Cousin
m) mein Haus
n) mein Ohr
o) mein Knie

Q3 a) mein Hund
b) ihr Bruder
c) mein Onkel
d) ihre Freundin
e) unser Cousin
f) mein Pferd
g) sein Vater
h) unsere Katze

Page 51

Q1

sie ———— she
du ———— they
er ———— we
es ———— you (informal singular)
wir ———— you (informal plural)
ihr ———— he
sie ———— it

Q2 b) Wir haben lange Haare.
c) Er ist hier.
d) Sie kauft Brot.
e) Wie alt ist er?

Q3 b) er c) sie d) er e) es

Page 52

Q1 b) das Getränk
c) die Schwester
d) den Monat
e) die Maus
f) das Jahr
g) die Speisekarte
h) das Schloss
i) den Blumenkohl
j) die Kuh
k) das Brot
l) den Morgen
m) die Schildkröte
n) das Hemd
o) die Katze
p) den Hund
q) die Briefmarke
r) das Kleid
s) den Tag
t) den Pfirsich
u) die Bäckerei
v) den Vogel
w) das Kaninchen
x) das Pferd

Q2 b) ein Eis
c) einen Keks
d) eine Bluse
e) eine Zwiebel
f) ein T-Shirt
h) meine Adresse
i) meinen Bruder
j) meine Orange
k) meinen Mantel
l) mein Ei
n) kein Steak
o) keine Brille
p) keine Postkarte
q) keinen Pullover
r) keinen Schinken

Q3 a) ein e) meinen
b) einen f) meine
c) keine g) kein
d) eine h) keine

Page 53

Q1 b) dem Hotel
c) dem Museum
d) dem Hamster
e) dem Reis
f) dem Briefkasten
g) dem Bahnhof
h) der Metzgerei
i) der Kartoffel
j) der Bank
k) der Hose
l) den Erbsen
m) dem Krankenhaus
n) dem Apfelsaft
o) der Tomate
p) dem Kopfsalat
q) der Konditorei
r) dem Rathaus

Answers

Q2 b) einer Erdbeere
    c) einem Wagen
    d) einer Speisekarte
    e) einem Bier
    f) einem Kellner
    h) meinem Hemd
    i) meinem Hund
    j) meiner Karte
    k) meinem Rock
    l) meiner Stadt
    n) keinem Theater
    o) keiner Wurst
    p) keinem Abendessen
    q) keinem Joghurt

Q3 a) Ich wohne in der Stadt.
    b) Frau Weber geht zur Bäckerei.
    c) Der Kaffee ist auf dem Tisch.
    d) Wir fahren zum Schloss.
    e) Die Bibliothek ist gegenüber der Post.
    f) Der Brief ist von der Frau.
    g) Ist sie im Kino?
    h) Ich fahre mit der Familie.
    i) Er ist an der Schule.

Page 54
Q1 a) gelb   d) grün
    b) groß   e) gut
    c) alt

Q2 a) gelbe
    b) große
    c) alte
    d) grüne
    e) gute

Q3 a) gelbes
    b) großer
    c) alte
    d) grüne
    e) guter

Q4 a) Das grüne Kleid.
    b) Eine grüne Erbse.
    c) Das alte Hemd.
    d) Die Hose ist groß.
    e) Ein grüner Pulli.
    f) Die Jacke ist blau.

Page 55
Q1
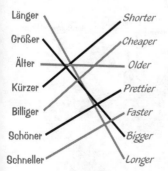

Q2 a) größte
    b) interessanteste
    c) älteste
    d) schnellste
    e) billigste

Q3 a) Dave ist größer als Geoff.
    b) Smita ist kürzer als Julie.
    c) James ist kleiner als Sandy.
    d) Kathy ist langsamer als Sarah.
    e) Geoff ist jünger als Suresh.
    f) Hans ist älter als Karl.
    g) Lisa ist netter als Polly.
    h) Thomas ist schneller als Dieter.

Page 56
Q1 a) Sie   h) Sie
    b) du   i) du
    c) du   j) du
    d) Sie
    e) Sie
    f) ihr
    g) du

Q2 a) Your mum: Wie heißt du?
    b) Policeman: Wie alt sind Sie?
    c) Man on the street: Sprechen Sie Deutsch?
    d) Your uncle: Bist du verheiratet?
    e) Best friend: Wie alt bist du ?

Q3 a) Wie alt bist du?
    b) Wo wohnst du?
    c) Wie haissen Sie?
    d) Wo wohnt Sie?
    e) Sprechen Sie Deutsch?

Page 57
Q1 a) frage
    b) fragst
    c) fragt
    f) fragen
    g) fragt
    h) fragen

Q2 a) kaufe
    b) versteht
    c) kaufen
    d) fragst
    e) spielen
    f) macht

Q3 a) ich esse
       du isst
       er isst
       wir essen
       ihr esst
       Sie essen

    b) ich fahre
       du fährst
       er fährt
       wir fahren
       ihr fahrt
       Sie fahren

    c) ich schlafe
       du schläfst
       er schläft
       wir schlafen
       ihr schlaft
       Sie schlafen

Q4 a) Ich fahre
    b) Sie spielen Fußball.
    c) Sie sieht fern.
    d) Sie lesen Bücher.
    e) Wir fragen.

Page 58
Q1 a) ich bin
       du bist
       er/sie/es ist
       wir sind
       ihr seid
       Sie sind
       sie sind

    b) ich habe
       du hast
       er/sie/es hat
       wir haben
       ihr habt
       Sie haben
       sie haben

Q2 b) anrufen
    c) ankommen
    d) abfahren
    e) abwaschen
    f) aussehen

Q3 a) Wir gehen aus.
    b) Ihr steht um sechs Uhr auf.
    c) Peter kommt um neun Uhr an.
    d) Du rufst Sarah an.
    e) Sie fahren um drei Uhr ab.
    f) Meine Mutter wascht ab.

Q4 a) Sie stehen auf.
    b) Er geht aus.
    c) Sie ruft an.
    d) Wir fahren ab.
    e) Sie kommen an.
    f) Wir waschen ab.

Page 59
Q1
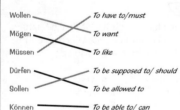

Q2 b) Sie wollen
    c) du kannst
    d) wir können
    e) er darf

Q3 a) Peter kann essen.
    b) Sie mögen Hunde.
    c) Ich soll schreiben.
    e) Ich muss Spanien visitieren.

Q4 a) Ich will schlafen.
    b) Ich mag Tischtennis spielen.
    c) Darf ich ausgehen?
    d) Ich soll abwaschen.

Answers

Page 60

Q1   ONE PERSON (FRIENDLY):
      Hör, Komm, Lauf
  TWO OR MORE (FRIENDLY):
      Singt, Setzt, Kommt
  ANY NUMBER (POLITE):
      Lesen, Nehmen, Treten, Sprechen

Q2 a) Don't sing!
    b) Don't run!
    c) Don't come!
    d) Don't speak!
    e) Don't read!
    f) Don't listen!
    g) Don't sit!

Q3 a) Singt!
    b) Sprechen Sie nicht!
    c) Seid ruhig!
    d) Setzt euch!
    e) Geh!
    f) Singen Sie nicht!
    g) Komm!
    h) Geht nicht!

Page 61

Q1 a) Er hat heute geschlafen.
    b) Sie hat es gebrochen.
    c) Wir haben gekocht.
    d) Ich habe einen Apfel gekauft.
    e) Du hast deine Mutter gesehen.
    f) Ich habe Tennis gespielt.

Q2 b) gefragt   f) geschrieben
    c) gehört   g) gesagt
    d) gegessen   h) gekauft
    e) getrunken i) gemacht

Q3 Ich habe Fußball gespielt.
    Ich habe gegessen.
    Ich habe Milch gekauft.
    Ich habe einen Brief an Dieter
    geschrieben.
    Ich habe Apfelsaft getrunken.

Page 62

Q1 b) Ich fahre nächstes Jahr nach Spanien.
    c) Du kommst nächste Woche hierhin.
    d) Du machst das am Montag.

Q2 ich werde   wir werden
    du wirst   ihr werdet
    er/sie/es wird   Sie werden
                   sie werden

Q3 a) Ich werde am Samstag singen.
    b) Er wird Sie morgen besuchen.
    c) Sie wird nächste Woche nach
        Spanien fahren.
    d) Ich werde nächstes Jahr nach
        Portugal fahren.
    e) Ich werde morgen putzen.
    f) Sie werden morgen schlafen.

Page 63

Q1 NEGATIVES:
    Ich mag käse nicht.
    Ich bin nicht sportlich.
    Ich spiele nicht gern Fußball.

POSITIVES:
    Sie ist meine Mutter.
    Das Haus ist gelb.
    Sie ist Sabine.

Q2

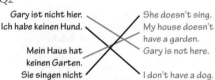

Gary ist nicht hier. — Gary is not here.
Ich habe keinen Hund. — I don't have a dog.
Mein Haus hat keinen Garten. — My house doesn't have a garden.
Sie singen nicht — She doesn't sing.

Q3 b) Die Lampe ist nicht rot.
       (The lamp is not red.)
    c) Ich habe keinen Bruder. (I have no
       brother. / I don't have a brother.)
    d) Sie ist nicht meine Mutter.
       (She is not my mother.)
    e) Bettina isst keinen Apfel.
       (Bettina eats no apple. / Bettina does
       not eat an apple.)
    f) Ich bin nicht Spanier.
       (I am not Spanish.)

Page 64

Q1 a) Ich habe Hunger.
    b) Ich spiele heute Fußball.
    c) Du hast heute kein Essen.
    e) Ich gehe ins Kino.
    f) Ich trinke Tee.
    g) Sie ist Berlinerin.

Q2 a) und   b) und
    c) aber   d) oder
    e) aber   f) oder

Q3 a) Heute spielen sie Fußball.
    b) Heute habe ich Hunger.
    c) Am Montag spiele ich Klavier
    d) Heute hast du kein Essen.
    e) Samstags liest sie.

Page 65

Q1

weil — because
wenn — if
obwohl — although

Q2 b) Ich koche nicht gern, obwohl Essen
       toll ist.
    c) Ich habe Hunger, weil ich heute
       morgen Fußball gespielt habe.
    d) Meine Mutter spielt Fußball, obwohl
       es neblig ist.

Q3 b) Obwohl ich Kaffee mag, hasse ich
       Tee.
    c) Wenn ich um fünf Uhr aufstehe,
       trinke ich Kaffee.
    d) Weil sie ins Kino gehen, rufen sie ein
       Taxi an.

Page 66

Q1 PRESENT TENSE — SPIELEN
    ich spiele   wir spielen
    du spielst   ihr spielt
    er/sie/es spielt   Sie spielen
                   sie spielen

PAST TENSE — KAUFEN
ich habe gekauft
du hast gekauft
er/sie/es hat gekauft
wir haben gekauft
ihr habt gekauft
Sie haben gekauft
sie haben gekauft

FUTURE TENSE — SCHWIMMEN
ich werde schwimmen
du wirst schwimmen
er/sie/es wird schwimmen
wir werden schwimmen
ihr werdet schwimmen
Sie werden schwimmen
sie werden schwimmen

PRESENT TENSE — TO BE
ich bin   wir sind
du bist   ihr seid
er/sie/es ist   Sie sind
             sie sind

Q2 THE DEFINITE ARTICLE

Nom. der	die	das	die
Acc. den	die	das	die
Dat. dem	der	dem	den

KEIN, KEINE, KEIN

Nom. kein	keine	kein	keine
Acc. keinen	keine	kein	keine
Dat. keinem	keiner	keinem	keinen

THE POSSESSIVE ADJECTIVES
mein dein sein ihr   sein
unser euer Ihr   ihr

Page 67

Page 68

die Gitarre, die Jacke, der Schlüssel, das Fahrrad, der Fisch, das Zelt, der Tisch, der Stuhl, das Buch, die Maus, die Katze, die Trompette, der Hund, der Apfel, die Banane, der Brief, der Schuh, die Brille